THE
SPACE-AGE
PHOTOGRAPHIC
ATLAS

THE
SPACE-AGE
PHOTOGRAPHIC
ATLAS

Compiled by Ken Fitzgerald

Equator

Australia

CROWN PUBLISHERS, INC.
New York

Library of Congress Catalog Card Number: 70-93399

Printed in the United States of America.

Published simultaneously in Canada by General Publishing Company Limited.

Map for title-page photograph:

From weather satellites man's view of the earth is continuous. The 156-picture photomontage of the globe was assembled from data transmitted by ESSA 3 during a single day. The latitude and longitude grid was automatically added by computer processing as each picture was received. Weather patterns photographed by satellite can be stored and referred to for long-term climatological studies. In the Northern Hemisphere storm vortexes, like the one in the montage, rotate counterclockwise. In the Southern Hemisphere such cyclonic patterns are clockwise.

ESSA Photo

ACKNOWLEDGMENTS

The credit lines for the photographs in this book are only a small indication of the many persons in government and industry who contributed to this volume by their daily work. Photographers, pilots, technicians, cartographers, and office workers in the United States, Canada, and other countries are part of a veritable army working toward increasing man's knowledge of his planet.

For reducing the size of my task, thanks in particular to: Les Gaver, Chief, Audio Visual Branch, Public Information Division, National Aeronautics and Space Administration; the staff of the Technology Application Center, University of New Mexico; Stewart Pardee, Fairchild Space and Defense Systems; and Erik Dahle, Chief, Cartography Section, Resources and Transport Division, United Nations.

All maps drawn by the author

PHOTOGRAPH CREDIT ABBREVIATIONS

ASCS	Agricultural Stabilization and Conservation Service
ESSA	Environmental Science Services Administration
NAPL	National Air Photo Library, Surveys and Mapping Branch, Department of Energy, Mines and Resources (Canada)
NASA	National Aeronautics and Space Administration
SCS	Soil Conservation Service
USCGS	United States Coast and Geodetic Survey
USDA	United States Department of Agriculture
USFS	United States Forest Service

CONTENTS

How to Use This Atlas

This book is more than a collection of aerial photographs taken by the Gemini astronauts, from Apollo spacecraft, by satellites, and from aircraft. It is a new kind of atlas, an atlas for the age of flight — above, and through, the atmosphere.

The photographs show more detail than is possible to portray on a map of comparable size. Thus the photographs have to be examined with more care than an ordinary map because nothing is omitted. A given site, however important, is shown in its surroundings as it is, without any particular emphasis through the use of large type, color, and so on.

For those unaccustomed to aerial photographs and unfamiliar with the earth sciences, two appendixes give summaries of these topics. Furthermore, each photograph is described with emphasis on key features of the landscape. It is important to remember that aerial photographs are "natural" views of the earth, and north is not always at the top of the picture. The key maps accompanying the photographs serve as an orientation guide and visual aid to interpretation of the pictures.

Millions of photographs have been taken of the earth, yet only the United States, Canada, Europe, and what were once colonial territories have been extensively mapped from the air. Only one-fifth of the land area of the world has been adequately mapped at all, according to professional cartographers. A series of conferences, sponsored by the United Nations and its specialized agencies, has been held in the past few years for the exchange of technical knowledge on aerial photography and its uses. Photogrammetry, a combination of optics and geometry, is a science using aerial photography for mapping purposes; cartography is the drafting of the maps themselves; both are expanding fields of endeavor in every nation of the world.

The photographs in this book are but a sampling of the millions in files maintained by governments and air-survey firms. Furthermore, the many Gemini and Apollo astronauts' pictures are but a selection of the thousands taken. The air traveler, the student, the scientist, and the armchair adventurer will find the broad representation of political areas, terrain, cities, and landforms in this book a guide to a better understanding of our planet.

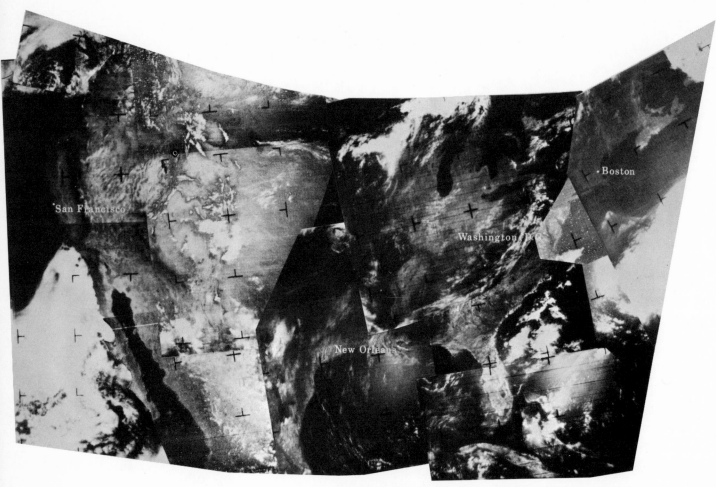

In this Nimbus 2 photomontage of the central section of North America, it is fair weather. The few clouds show how weather patterns follow land and sea forms.

NASA

Part I
NORTH AMERICA

A general description of the continent would be that it is a broad plain with mountain belts to the east and west, nearly surrounded by the sea. It lies in the north-middle latitudes, has a variety of climates and vegetation, and is of comparatively recent extensive occupation by man.

Geographically, North America embraces Canada and the coterminous United States, as well as Alaska, Mexico, Greenland, and the French territory of Saint-Pierre-et-Miquelon. Central America is part of the larger continental mass but is considered a separate entity by reason of its culture and tropical location.

About 200 million years ago, North America, with Europe and part of Africa, was a single huge landmass geologists call Laurasia. The transformation of this precontinent into the land areas we know is described by the continental-drift theory. Visible evidence of the continuance of drift in North America is in the growing separation of the Baja California peninsula from mainland Mexico.

The continent has an area of about nine million square miles (23.3 million square kilometers) and an estimated population of just under 300 million. Most of the people live in urban areas, including the world's largest: the New York metropolitan area.

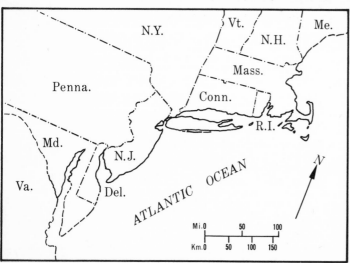

Half of the original United States is shown in this single TIROS 7 photograph. Early settlements on the protected harbors from Massachusetts Bay to Delaware Bay are now major cities. Inland, the early barrier mountains, the Appalachians, can be traced by low-lying clouds along their ridgelines.

United States

Northeastern United States

The Atlantic coast, from Cape Cod south, is a low-lying plain whose rocks are mostly sedimentary deposits borne seaward by the region's rivers. To the north, ancient lava flows and other once-molten rock have been laid bare when less-resistant sediments covering them were eroded away. Northward through New England the coastline becomes increasingly rugged where the sea overran the land to leave rocky hilltops standing above the water.

Along Cape Cod, Long Island, New Jersey, and the shore south to Florida, narrow coastal-barrier islands have been built up by ocean currents shifting sand along the shore.

Inland from the coastal plain lie the Appalachian Mountains, the eastern mountain border to North America. They begin in the Maritime Provinces of Canada, and run southeasterly to end as the Great Smoky Mountains of Tennessee and North Carolina and the hills of Alabama. But the roots of this once higher chain can be traced as far as western Texas.

From east to west the Appalachian chain is made up of three major geomorphological or landform types. In the case of these mountains, the much-eroded crystalline rocks of the "Older" Appalachians slope down to and under the coastal plain. Separated by the Great Valley are the "Newer" Appalachians whose much-folded ridges are composed of layers of sedimentary material. Farthest west is the level-topped Allegheny or Appalachian Plateau, which is called the Cumberland Plateau to the south.

The Appalachian system is a complex region whose present appearance is the result of three massive orogenic, or folding, sequences separated in time by uplift, nearly complete erosion to a plain, invasion by volcanoes, intrusion by pluton-ic masses, and glaciation in the north. The sequence began about 400 million years ago, was renewed about 350 million years ago, and molded to the present stage about 225 million years ago.

Geographically, the Appalachians begin with the folded ranges of southern New York and Pennsylvania, but geologically, the Taconic, Green Mountains, White Mountains, and peaks in Maine and the Maritime Provinces are part of the chain. On a worldwide scale the Appalachians can be traced to Scotland, indicating their origin before the opening of the Atlantic Ocean.

MAINE

Mount Desert Island

The granite mountains of Mount Desert are made of once-molten rock that had forced its way upward through sediments still present in the Southern Appalachians. As we see Mount Desert today, the sedimentary overburden has been eroded away completely. That this happened before the most recent Ice Age is proved by the

The eastern half of Mount Desert Island, Maine, is an isolated group of granitic knobs. Cadillac Mountain is the highest on the eastern seacoast. Bar Harbor, the principal settlement, has been a favorite resort of Americans and Canadians for many years. All the lakes and ponds lie in glacially carved valleys.

USCGS-ESSA

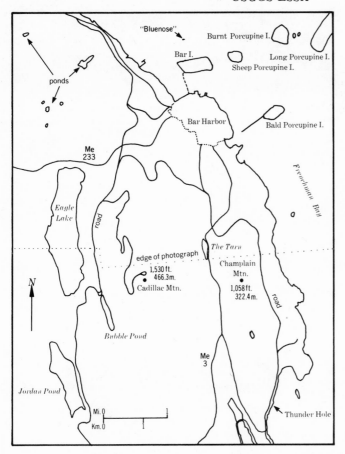

glacially carved valleys and impounded lakes dammed by glacial debris from higher slopes.

As much as any other area, Mount Desert shows the never stagnant outer surface of the earth in transition. The island, higher but typical of the Maine coast, is a piece of elevated ground sinking into the sea. Offshore, in the Gulf of Maine, rugged underwater topography like that of the island shows the region was once dry land. Geologists call this a coastline of submergence. In contrast, on the other side of the continent, southern California is a coastline of emergence where old beaches lie high up on hillsides.

The greater part of the area shown in the aerial photomosaic is part of Acadia National Park. This was the first National Park to be established east of the Mississippi, and the first donated to the Federal Government. It was named Isle des Mont Deserts in 1604 by its discoverer, Samuel de Champlain. The preponderance of French names on geographical features commemorates Sieur de la Mothe Cadillac (founder of Detroit, governor of Louisiana, and once a resident of the island); Acadia (French North America, which Champlain explored for King Henry IV of France); and at one time Lafayette (the park was originally called Lafayette National Park in honor of the Marquis, a friend of Cadillac's granddaughter and once a local landowner).

In 1901 a number of summer residents formed a conservation landholding group that turned its property over to the Federal Government, and in 1919 President Woodrow Wilson signed the act creating the park.

Prominent in the mosaic is the north-south direction of much of the terrain, an indication of the direction taken by the ice sheet. Geologically, the mountain trend is east-west, which shows the power of the ice when it crossed this area last about 20 thousand years ago. The diagonal cracks are fractures in the granite mass that will widen as the mountains decompose.

NEW HAMPSHIRE

White Mountain National Forest

Climate, altitude, and unshielded exposure to the elements make Mount Washington an arctic island in the middle-latitude temperate zone of the United States. Only Mount Mitchell, at the southern end of the Appalachian chain, is higher (by about 350 feet [106.6 meters]) in the mountains east of the Mississippi. The southern peak, however, is in a more moderate climatic zone.

The chill of New England winters is felt all year on Mount Washington, where snow falls in every month. Like the rest of the northern Appalachians, the White Mountains were once buried under thick layers of sediment. Erosion removed the sedimentary rock, and the great ice sheet cut narrow valleys known locally as "notches."

Mount Washington is composed of metamorphosed sedimentary and volcanic rock — remnants of folding more than 350 million years ago. Other mountains of the Presidential Range are a complex structure of intruded magmas from deep in the earth's crust plus solidified lava formed between 400 and 225 million years ago. Some of this differing structure is visible at ground level on the sides of the notches.

The Great Gulf, Tuckerman Ravine, and Oakes Gulf on the mountainside are cirques — bowl-shaped valleys formed at the heads of glaciers when the ice first cut them out of the mountains.

The exposed position of Mount Washington not only gives it an arctic climate the year round but also some of the fiercest weather in a region noted for harsh winters. The world's greatest wind velocity — 231 miles per hour (371.75 kilometers per hour) was recorded at the weather station atop the mountain. Even in midsummer, hikers are warned not to venture on the upper trails without protective clothing.

As part of the National Forest System, the White Mountains are regulated for multiple use. Logging, mining, and recreation are the main activities. The region is maintained as a center of outdoor activity by the Appalachian Mountain Club, which keeps in condition trails, huts, and shelters.

High in the Presidential Range of the White Mountains lies the Great Gulf, one of several cirques, or bowl-shaped valleys, in the area. Each cirque was once filled by the head of an individual glacier. In the photograph, the terminus of the cog railway, automobile road, and buildings at the summit give a sense of scale.

USFS-USDA

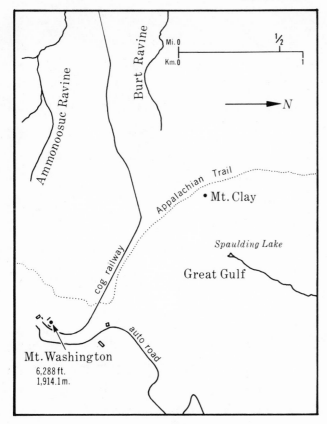

Laconia

The importance of climate in the shaping of mountains is impressively shown by contrasting the northern and southern sections of the Appalachian Mountains. In cool New England, where snowmelt fills the rivers in spring, the peaks are sharp, the lakes many and often, large, like Lake Winnipesaukee. Also the deep, narrow, glacially carved or rock-fracture valleys and scoured, bare rock outcrops make for a dramatic landscape.

In the south, from the Potomac River Valley to Alabama, the warm humid climate helps form rounded tree-covered slopes with very few lakes except those made by artificial dams.

The New England and New York State lakes are so much the result of glacial action that their alignment is often an indication of the direction in which the ice moved. In New York, the Finger Lakes and Lake Champlain, on the border with Vermont, are particularly striking examples of water-filled deep glacial valleys. Lake Champlain also lies in a fault trough. In New Hampshire, Lake Winnipesaukee is what might be called a compound lake, carved by the glacier, filling large fractures in the rock, and dammed by glacial debris. This lake sits astride a low dome of mostly granitic rock that cooled, below the land surface, between 500 million to 225 million years ago. The dome is not solid but a complex structure with metamorphic rock — molten rock and sedimentary rock whose character was changed by heat and pressure — mixed with intrusive granite bodies, some volcanic material and basic material from deep in the crust of the earth.

Water from Lake Winnipesaukee provides much of the flow of the Merrimack River. It is the waterpower from the Merrimack that provided the basis for the 200-year-old industrial complex from Lowell, Massachusetts, to Concord, New Hampshire. The lake is also one of the state's natural tourist attractions, drawing thousands of visitors at all seasons.

This aerial mosaic of the Lake Winnipesaukee resort area shows the southeasterly movement taken by the ice sheet and great fractures in the bedrock that the lake fills. The lake supplies some of the water for the Merrimack River, along whose valley lies the oldest stretch of industry in the country.

SCS-USDA

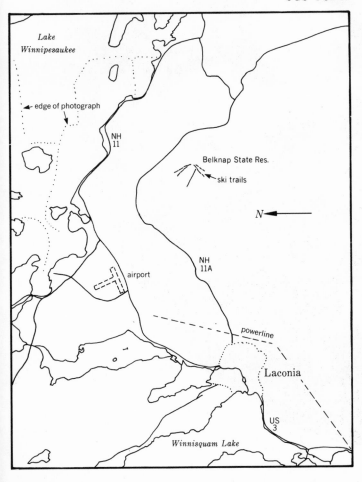

MASSACHUSETTS

Boston

Aerial photography began in the mid-nineteenth century with the simultaneous development of man-carrying balloons and the camera. Both were quickly put to use for military reconaissance and for surveying. Credit for the first practical adaptation of the camera as a precision aerial recorder belongs to Colonel Aimé Laussedat, of the French Army Engineer Corps, who used kite-borne cameras in 1858.

The oldest aerial photograph still in existence is this *Balloon-view of Boston, Mass., 1860*. The principal landmark still standing in the area covered is Old South Meetinghouse, built in 1729. It is now a museum. Today Washington Street is lined with department stores, shops, and theatres. East, to the harbor, is now part of Boston's commercial and financial district.

Library of Congress

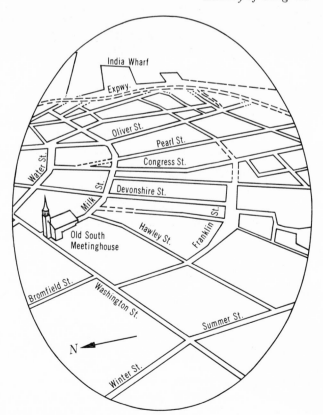

In the United States, an early aerial subject was Boston. On October 13, 1860, Samuel King and James Black took what is the oldest surviving aerial photograph from a tethered balloon 1,200 feet (365.7 meters) over Boston Common. In the picture, reproduced on the opposite page, only the Old South Meetinghouse, now a museum, remains as a prominent landmark. Most of the rest of the area shown in the photograph was destroyed by fire in 1872 or was demolished as the city grew.

During the Civil War, both armies — particularly the Union Army with its Corps of Aeronautics — used tethered balloons for reconnaissance and photography. Analysis of aerial photographs broadened from a military occupation, and photo interpretation is now used in urban studies, forestry, geology, hydrology, oceanography, civil engineering, agriculture, archaeology, and other fields.

Photography from aircraft began with a demonstration motion picture taken in Italy from a plane piloted by Wilbur Wright on April 24, 1909. Military use of aerial photography begain in World War I, was improved in World War II, and today is combined with specialized radar and other electronic remote sensors from aircraft and satellites. But the most spectacular results have come from the Gemini and Apollo spacecraft flights whose photographs, as dramatic as they are utilitarian, are a new way of looking at our planet.

Panoramic view of the New London-Groton area covers 180 degrees. The apparent curvature of the horizon is an effect of the camera's complex lens system. From side to side it encompasses a view about 12½ miles (20.11 kilometers) wide, and fades into the distance of about 7 miles (11.26 kilometers).

Fairchild Space and Defense Systems

CONNECTICUT

New London-Groton

In their attempt to get the widest possible coverage in a single photograph with maximum clarity and minimum processing, photographic engineers have developed several types of complex camera systems. The accompanying photograph of New London and Groton was taken with a camera using a rotating double prism to project the image onto a moving strip of film. By means of an elaborate electronic control circuit, compensation for the speed of the aircraft is built in. The film and prism are moved in a precise relationship to give 180-degree horizon-to-horizon coverage. A special transparent grid overlay is used for interpretation of local angles of roads, buildings, and so on.

Although developed for military use, the system has obvious advantages for rapid, wide coverage of flooded areas, pollution control, crop studies, and the like.

The area shown in the photograph is the mouth of the Thames River, with New London to the left and Groton to the right. New London was one of the early deepwater ports in the state, and the gateway to eastern Connecticut. It served as a port for privateers during the Revolution and as an important base for whaling ships for sixty years afterward. The "neutral ground" of the Thames River is the site of the annual Yale-Harvard crew races, which end above the prominent bridge in the photograph.

Today New London is best known as the home of the United States Coast Guard Academy and for the United States Navy Submarine Base. On the opposite shore, Groton is also an important

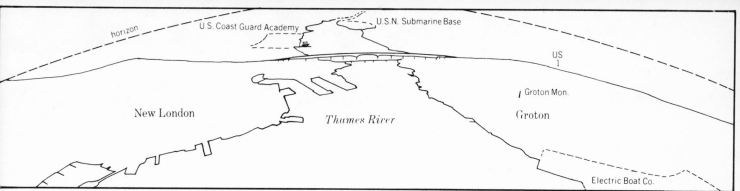

submarine port. The Electric Boat Division of General Dynamics Corporation, where the first nuclear-powered submarine, the *Nautilus,* was built, has its yards on the river. The firm got its curious name early in the century when battery-powered undersea craft were first designed and built. Many vessels of the American nuclear-powered undersea fleet were produced at the Groton yard.

Groton was the scene of a massacre in 1791 when Tories, led by Benedict Arnold, overran Fort Griswold and killed their prisoners. The Groton Monument, visible in the photograph, is 135 feet tall (41.14 meters), and shows the detail possible in a panoramic photograph of this type.

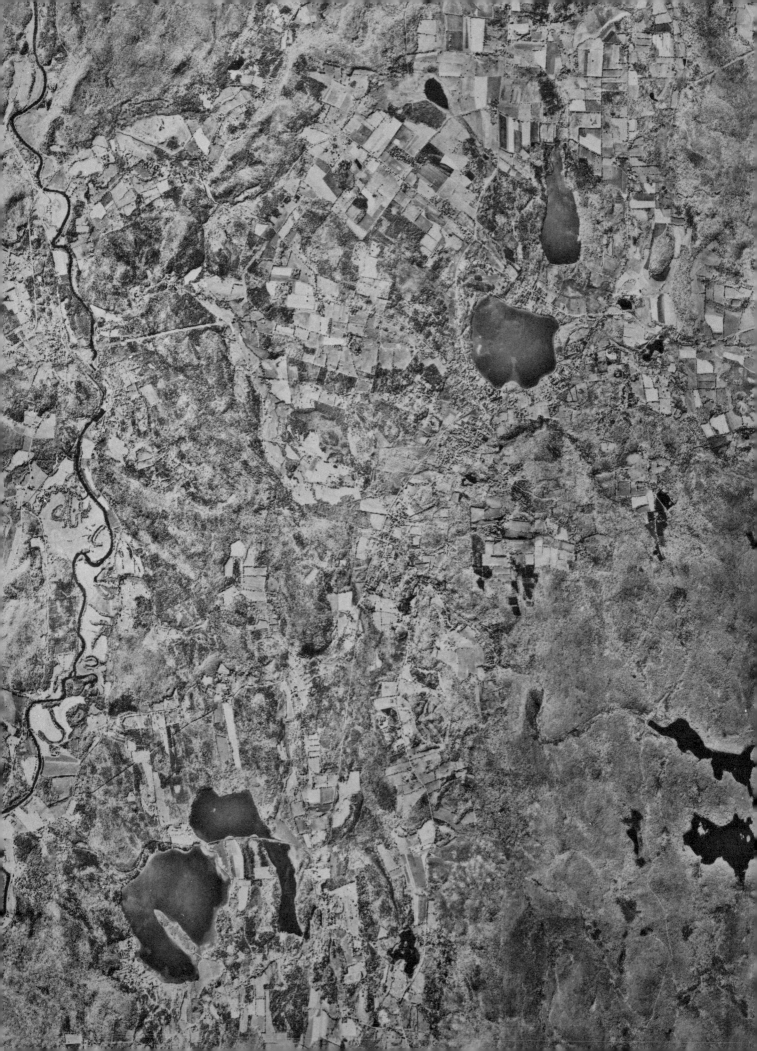

Litchfield County

Some measure of the economic and industrial changes in the United States are apparent in the northwest corner of Connecticut. The region shown in the accompanying aerial mosaic was one of the country's leading industrial and mining sites early in the eighteenth century.

Salisbury, settled by the Dutch from the Hudson River valley in 1720, became a boomtown in the 1730s when iron was discovered on nearby Mount Riga. The mines had a peak of production

during the Revolution, but operations dwindled when more accessible deposits were found in New York, New Jersey, and Pennsylvania. Today Mount Riga is less than a ghost town: A small cemetery, a crumbling iron furnace, and a few building foundations are all that remain.

The Litchfield Hills are a lower, southerly extension of both the Green Mountains of Vermont and the Taconic range of New York. The Housatonic River Valley divides the two ranges after they become the Berkshire Hills in Massachusetts. Once a source of power for local industry, the Housatonic today waters a region of small communities, resorts, and light manufacturing.

Mountains at the tristate corner of Connecticut-Massachusetts-New York are part of the Taconic Range. Called the Berkshires in Massachusetts, and the Litchfield Hills in Connecticut, they are a much folded, eroded, and glaciated region. Once an iron-producing area, this part of Litchfield County now has farms, estates, resorts, and small industry.

SCS-USDA

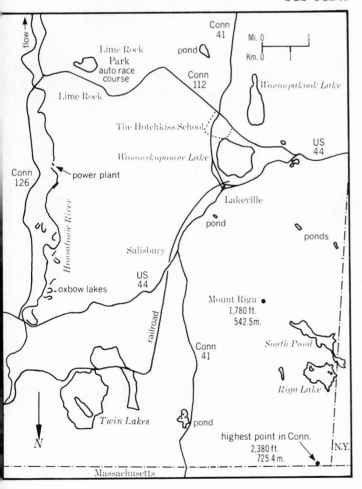

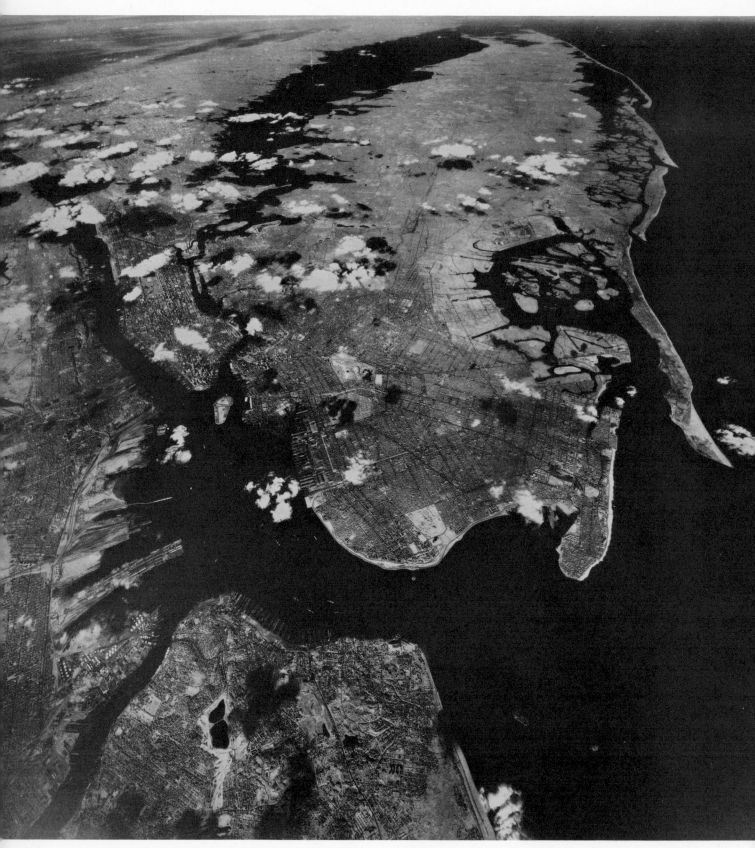

An advanced camera design was used to take this panorama. It shows the eastern half of the New York metropolitan area, including all of Long Island, in one photograph. The urbanization, large natural harbor, and topography of the region are evident.

Aero Service Division, Litton Industries

NEW YORK

New York City

The urban area of which New York City is the center is the world's largest. It lies nearly at the midpoint of the 400-mile (643.7-kilometer) stretch of closely packed cities and towns stretching from Boston to Washington, D.C.

In the accompanying photograph, the New York City boroughs (also counties) of Brooklyn (Kings), Queens (Queens), Manhattan (New York), and Staten Island (Richmond) seem nearly blanketed by buildings, streets, and industrial sites. The photograph also points out the reason for this: the well-protected harbor, the broad Hudson River leading into the agricultural center of the state, and access via the East River strait to Long Island Sound.

Geologically, New York City's metamorphic bedrock, particularly on Manhattan Island, is the most southerly approach of bare rock to the sea on the continent. From New York Bay south, the coastal plain extends a considerable distance inland, with its widest dimension in the Mississippi valley as far north as Illinois.

Long Island is composed entirely of erosion and glacial deposits, with the only relief being two ranges of hills formed at the foot of the ice sheet. These terminal moraines, as they are called by geomorphologists, divide to form the easternmost tips of the island. They are evident as a single range across Queens and Brooklyn, and extend into Staten Island and New Jersey.

Along the outer shore of Long Island, ocean currents have formed narrow sand barrier islands. Their role is to protect the shoreline, but storms and shifts in currents and bottom topography move great quantities of sand up and down the coast, despite man's efforts to stabilize the beaches. Sandspits at the ends of the islands arc away from the southerly long-shore currents as part of the shifting pattern of the coastline.

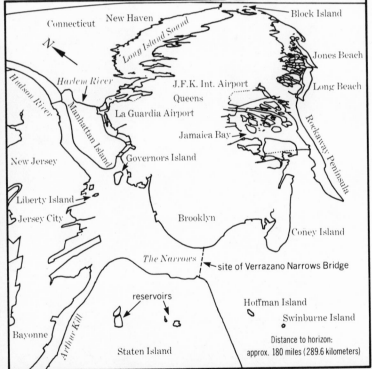

This panoramic view of the Verrazano-Narrows Bridge sweeps 180 degrees from Staten Island (left) to Brooklyn (right). Taken from 1,000 feet (304.8 meters) considerable detail is evident, including ripples in the wake of the large cargo vessel in the foreground.

Fairchild Space and Defense Systems

PENNSYLVANIA

McConnellsburg

The rocks of the newer Appalachian Mountains, which form a flat S curve from New York and Pennsylvania to Alabama, were once loose sand and silt deposited in a long trench between 600 and 350 million years ago. Then, in the ceaseless rhythm of geologic change, the mountains were lifted and warped into a complex series of ridges from 350 to 225 million years ago.

Later, erosion cut to the core of some ridges

Land utilization in the Appalachian Mountains is conditioned by the highly folded terrain. This aerial mosaic of part of Fulton County, Pennsylvania, shows a variety of field crops, evident in the patterned rural sections. Small towns lie in the valleys. Recent innovations in road building and more powerful vehicles have made areas like this more accessible for commerce, and tourists.

SCS-USDA

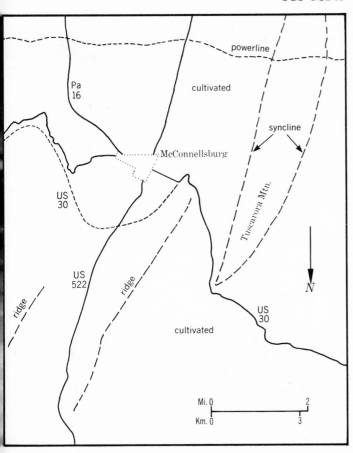

and dug deep into adjacent valleys. Scientific curiosity about the origin of these now highly eroded mountains was the principal spur to economic and scholarly geology in the United States during the nineteeth century. The eroded folds were typed: An upwarped or convex fold is an anticline; a fold in which the rock strata slope inward from both sides is a syncline. Reconstruction of the original level surface is often possible by tracing the sequence of strata over a wide area.

In utilizing the rugged anticline-syncline terrain for farms and industry, the ridges were left to loggers and miners and the rich bottomlands of the valleys to the farmers. In the accompanying aerial mosaic of the northern Appalachians, this division of uses is apparent. Elsewhere in this atlas, in a view of Birmingham, Alabama, and in the photographs of the world's deserts, the same landforms are visible.

The drainage pattern in these mountains is of the trellis type. However, considerable irregularities exist, especially when one stream cuts into the valley drained by a second and captures as geologists term it, the waters of another stream. The second stream thus reverses part of its course, perhaps to alter the drainage pattern enough for yet another capture of a stream.

An abandoned stream channel across a mountain ridge is called a "wind gap." In other places the stream or river may continue its original course when it cuts across a ridge faster than the mountain is uplifted. These water gaps are one of the spectacular aspects of geology, one of the most famous being the Delaware Water Gap of Pennsylvania-New Jersey.

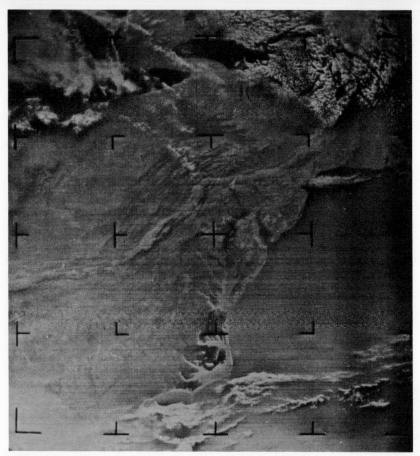

Much of the eastern seaboard of the United States, portions of southern Canada, and the Appalachian Mountains are covered by this Nimbus 1 photograph. It was taken by the weather satellite from an altitude of 430 miles (692.01 kilometers).

NASA

The Mid-Atlantic States

The influence of geography on human affairs is especially apparent in the contrast between the Northeast and Middle-Atlantic states. European colonists with similar national origins developed quite different viewpoints in the agricultural plain of the Mid-Atlantic region and in the rocky forests of New England.

Waterborne local commerce developed early on the wide shallow rivers leading off Chesapeake Bay. Inland, towns were laid out at the head of navigation or below the first waterfall or rapids. An arc of "fall line" cities extends from Trenton, New Jersey; through Baltimore, Maryland; Richmond, Virginia; Raleigh, North Carolina; Columbia, South Carolina; and Augusta, Macon, and Columbus, Georgia. Canal companies organized to dig waterways to the Ohio River became railroad operators after the first railroads were laid out on the coastal plain.

Prominent in the accompanying photograph is

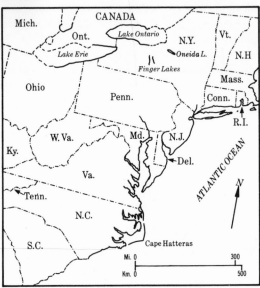

the arcing chain of barrier islands along the shallow waters of the coast. The reason for the regular curves of the offshore bars is not clear to geologists, and satellite photographs like the one above have emphasized the need for increased studies with a view to protection of the main shoreline.

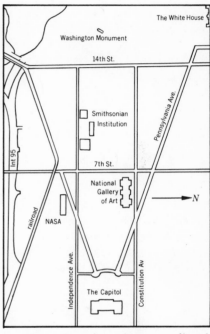

The Mall between the Capitol and the Washington Monument is shown in an enlargement from a high-altitude panorama. The camera automatically swept from horizon to horizon, giving single-picture coverage of a large area. The enlarged section was directly beneath the aircraft, and a vertical photograph is the result.

Perkin-Elmer Corporation

DISTRICT OF COLUMBIA

Washington

In aerial photographs of the United States capital, the gridiron street plan with its diagonal avenues is immediately apparent. Originally designed late in the eighteenth century by Pierre L'Enfant, Washington's street system was not completed until early in this century.

L'Enfant's plan for Washington was based on Sir Christopher Wren's scheme for rebuilding London after the Great Fire in 1666. Wren derived parts of his ideas from the garden at Versailles, which in turn was based on a Roman garden model. A myth has grown that the city of Washington was laid out after the radial street pattern used for Paris. But the French plan was devised for Napoleon III by Baron Georges Haussmann in the mid-nineteenth century.

As an urban view, the accompanying aerial photographs show the impressive openness and stately vistas of Washington; they also show the encroachment of highways, government buildings, and the ubiquitous parking lot.

WEST VIRGINIA

Philippi

West of the main Appalachian Mountain chain lies a broad plateau stretching from New York State to Alabama. Called the Allegheny or Appalachian Plateau from central West Virginia north and the Cumberland Plateau to the south, it shows what the Appalachians were like before they were folded.

From a viewpoint on top of the plateau, level-topped tree-covered mountains stretch to the horizon. The mountains themselves are made up

Strip mining of near-surface coal beds has been part of West Virginia's economy for a century. To rehabilitate old coal fields, aerial mosaics, such as this one of part of Barbour County, are useful in planning future land management.

SCS-USDA

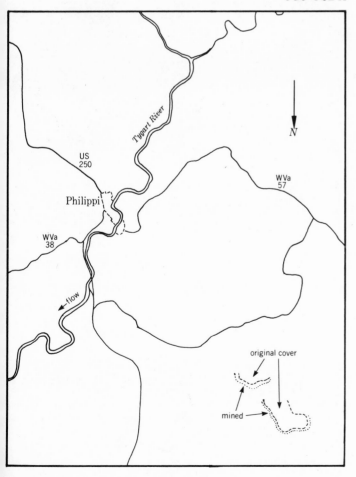

of thick beds of sediment laid down at the same time as the folded Appalachians, the difference being that the plateau sediments were laid over level ground whereas the Appalachian material filled a deep down-warped section of the earth's crust. Some of the sediments accumulated in humid coastal forests and swamps bordering shallow seas from 285 to 235 million years ago. The plants fell and decayed and the area subsided. Later sediments buried and compacted these ancient forests to form the extensive coal fields we find today. From Pennsylvania to Alabama, lignite, bituminous, and anthracite coal are dug from the plateau.

West Virginia ranks sixth among the coal-producing states in the country. The beds are often close enough to the surface for strip mining. When the soil and rock overburden is removed and the coal is dug out, runoff water gullies the slopes, silts the streams, and presents a cheerless, bleak landscape.

Pollution control, renewal of urban and rural areas, ecological factors determining the chain of future accumulation of water and food, and analysis of wasteful processes are all examined in part from aerial photographs like that shown here.

KENTUCKY

Mammoth Cave

The rare case in which underground geologic exploration is possible is in the caves of the world. Caves can be formed in lava when the surface hardens over a molten bubble and the semiliquid interior flows away. In sandstone, caves are formed by wave action fracturing weak sections of the sedimentary beds. But most of the world's important caves are found in limestone. The Mammoth Cave is the most well known of a series in the limestone region of Virginia, Kentucky, Indiana and Ohio.

Limestone caves are formed as rain and snowmelt percolate into and dissolve subsurface rock. Chemically, rainwater contains carbon dioxide combined with pure water. This acts on calcium carbonate in the limestone to form water-soluble calcium bicarbonate. One year's rainfall on one acre (.40 hectare) of land in the Mammoth Cave region can dissolve a cubic yard (.76 cubic meters) of rock.

The net effect is an irregular topography with many depressions called "sinkholes" on the surface, and underground caverns and waterways formed as the limestone is washed away. Inside the caves, water bearing minerals in solution drips from the roof, evaporates, and leaves the minerals to form the stalactites and stalagmites that decorate the caves.

As a sinkhole region matures, it ultimately becomes a pitted plain with low, eroded hills with flat tops. In humid climates, lakes form in the sinkholes when the land is near sea level. The chain of sinkhole lakes in central Florida shown in this atlas is a prominent example.

Mammoth Cave National Park preserves the dramatic underground caverns and also retains the natural forest of the sinkhole surface. Rectangular depressions and relief are indicative of limestone erosion along straight lines and sharp angles.

ASCS-USDA

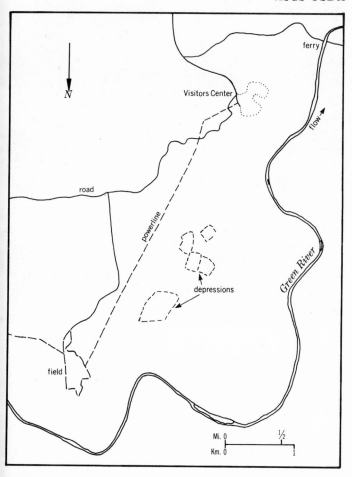

Cumulus clouds neatly outline the Florida peninsula. The gaps indicate warmer air rising over waterways and lakes, in this Gemini 5 photograph. A line of cloud growth follows the Atlantic shore from Jacksonville south in a sweep across the state. Three thunderstorms are prominent over Key West and the outer keys.

NASA

FLORIDA

The Florida peninsula is a low, upwarped arch composed mostly of limestone whose margins blend land and sea. Most of the state has an elevation of less than 65 feet (about 20 meters), and the highest point in the state is only 345 feet (105.15 meters) above sea level.

Erosion in the raised spine of the peninsula has created a chain of water-filled sinkholes and springs. The lakes and springs combine with the humid tropical climate and phosphate-rich soil to form the basis for the state's extensive agricultural industry.

Cape Kennedy — "The Cape" to millions of Americans involved with aerospace projects — is the site of the John F. Kennedy Space Center operated by the National Aeronautics and Space Administration. Photographs of the earth taken during Gemini and Apollo flights launched here have proved the value of space photography in earth-resources studies.

Geologically, The Cape is a foreland being built southward by sand drifting south along the shore.

From Lake Okeechobee south, Florida is a 5,000-square-mile (12,945-square-kilometer) marshland called the Everglades. These bars fringe the east side of the Everglades. These bars are an urban population center. At the coastline, the north-flowing current we call the Gulf Stream has cut an undersea precipice. Off Palm Beach, the ocean reaches a depth of over 650 feet (about 200 meters) only seven miles (11.2 kilometers) offshore. This contrasts with the shoal waters off the tip of the peninsula.

The southern edge of Lake Okeechobee is only about 17 feet (5.18 meters) above sea level. Cape Sable, 100 miles (160.9 kilometers) away, is barely above high tide. The Everglades in between is, in essence, a shallow, very wide, slowly flowing river. Of the marshland, 192 square miles (496.26 square kilometers) are in the Everglades National Park, and under some form of conservation control. Outside the park, water demands by coastal towns and for agriculture have heightened the effects of occasional drought, permitted the incursion of seawater, and led to the growth of pestilent mangrove swamps in the area.

South of the Florida peninsula, the sand and coral reef islands of the Florida Keys arc into the Gulf of Mexico to form the southernmost part of the United States.

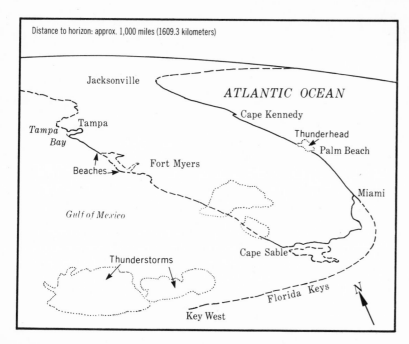

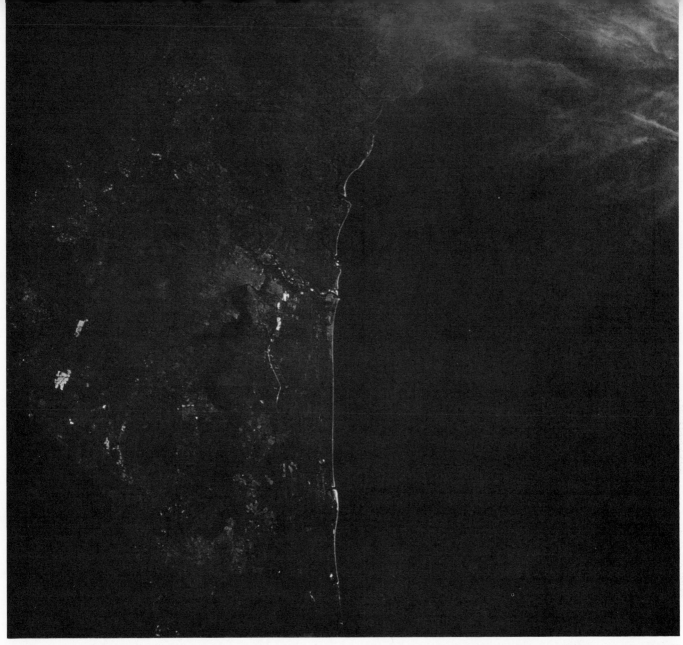

Jacksonville and the St. Johns River form Florida's chief port. Rail, highway, and air traffic combine with shipping to make the city a focus of trade for a large part of the southeastern United States. A trans-Florida canal, scheduled for completion in 1972, will cross the state from Jacksonville to the Gulf of Mexico.

NASA

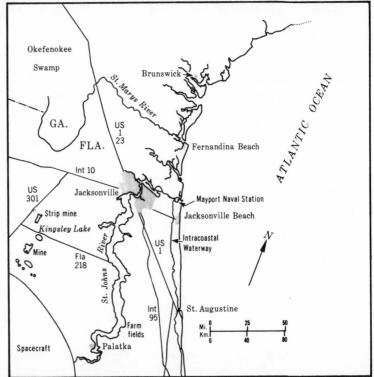

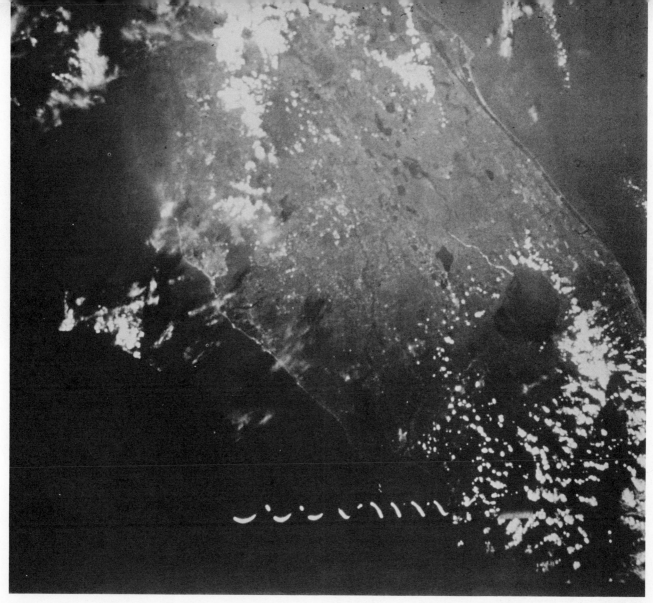

Water-filled sinkholes are a prominent feature in this view of central Florida. In less humid climates, or higher elevations, they would be dry and possibly suitable for agriculture. The photograph spans Florida from Tampa Bay to Cape Kennedy. Sebring is near the center.

NASA

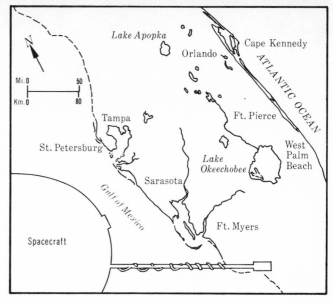

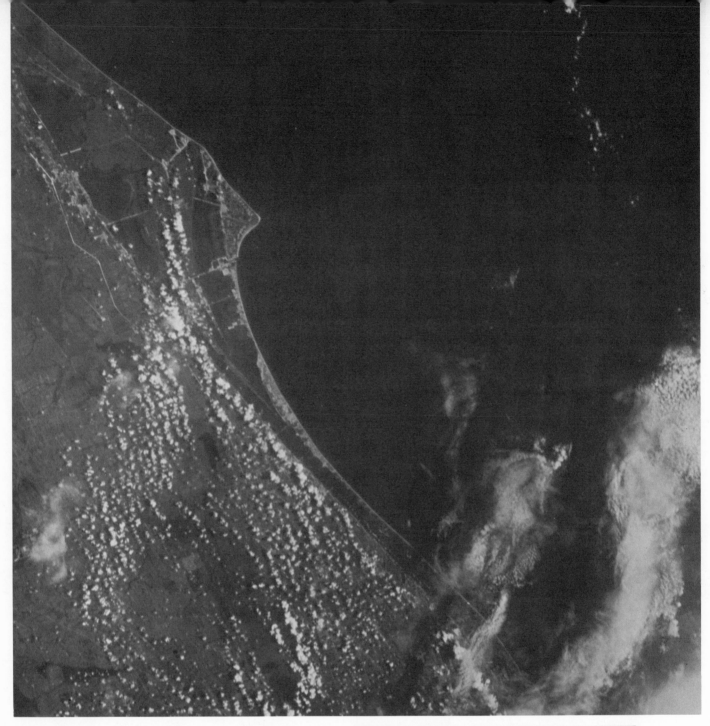

Cape Kennedy and the John F. Kennedy Space Center, launching site for the Gemini 5 astronauts who took this photograph, are shown here in great detail. Geologically, Cape Kennedy is a foreland being built seaward by sand borne by coastwise currents from the north. The Gulf Stream flows north along the coast but is farther out in the Atlantic.

NASA

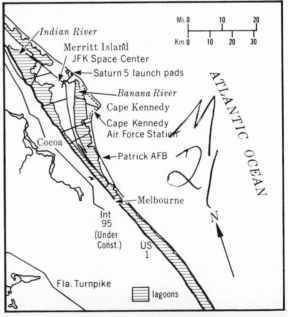

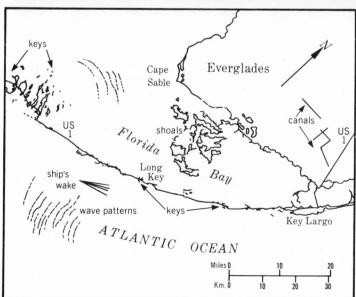

The oceanographic value of spacecraft photography is shown in this Gemini 4 photograph. Current patterns are revealed by the sun glint and movement of oil slicks. The general view is of Cape Sable, Everglades National Park, and some of the Florida Keys.

NASA

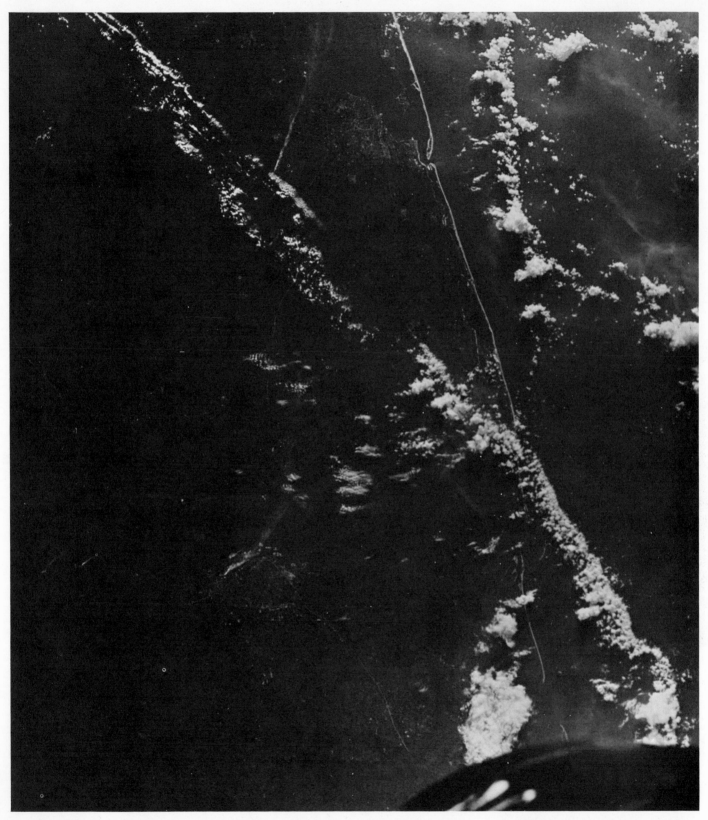

The Gulf Coast of Alabama and Florida is low, flat, and protected by offshore barrier beaches. They are very narrow in this section of the coast because of local current conditions. The industrial or utility plant smoke plumes visible in the photograph show how pollution particles can be carried great distances from their source.

NASA

ALABAMA

Mobile Bay

The shallow waters of Mobile Bay are the remnants of a much larger estuary that silted up in a short time, about three thousand years ago. Only about one-quarter of the original bay remains open. The deposits in the upper bay were carried downstream by the Tombigbee and Alabama rivers. As they empty into the bay, these rivers merge to form the many-channeled Mobile and Tensaw rivers.

One of the possible causes of rapid silting may be the local geologic structure. Both sides of the bay are faults marking the edges of a dropped section of underlying rock — a "graben," in geologic terms. The opposite case, where a section is raised, is called a "horst."

Aiding the silting today are the offshore barrier islands, which also act as a natural breakwater for the state's only seaport.

Birmingham

As the "Pittsburgh of the South," Birmingham takes advantage of nearby coal and iron ore deposits for iron and steel production. Manufactures from these raw materials also make the city an industrial and metalworking center.

Birmingham lies very close to the southern end of the Appalachian chain near where the folded mountains disappear beneath the coastal-plains deposits from rivers flowing into the Gulf of Mexico. Geological studies of the area show it once to have been on the edge of a great trough of crustal rock. Such a depression is called a geosyncline.

The city lies in a tightly compressed, highly folded and eroded segment of the Appalachians, which can be seen in the Apollo 9 photograph. Unraveling the rock sequence and datings its convolutions is one of the more ingenious aspects

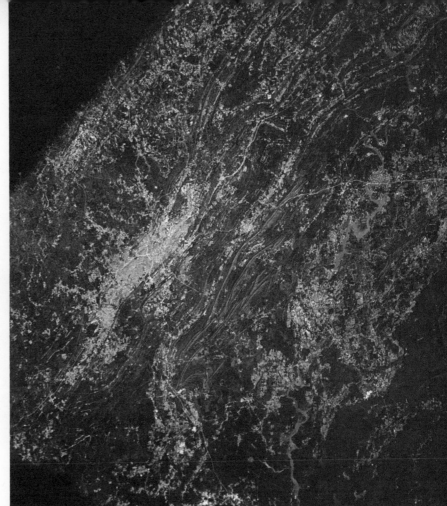

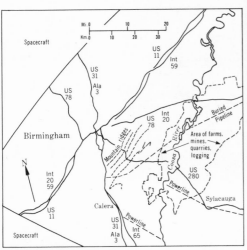

This Apollo 9 photograph is a striking example of geographic influences on man. Birmingham neatly outlines one of the ridges of the tightly compressed folds of the southern Appalachians. Nearby, the strip-mining operations of the Coosa River valley indicate the economic value of this industrial section of the south.

NASA

of geology. In sedimentary rocks, fossil remains and radiometric dating are the geologists' chief tools. To many, fossils conjure up a picture of dinosaurs, but the era of these reptiles was only one in the history of life on earth. Many fossils are the remains of only microscopic creatures.

The great coal beds of Alabama, as elsewhere, were formed when vegetation from ancient swamps and forests was buried under layers of eroded silt. Pressure and chemical reactions slowly altered the plant life to one of the several forms of coal.

In this aerial mosaic of part of Birmingham, some of the city's industrial complex is visible. A minor ridge of the Appalachians shows the mountains' trend through the city. The curved, light-colored area is the path of construction for part of the Interstate Highway System.

ASCS-USDA

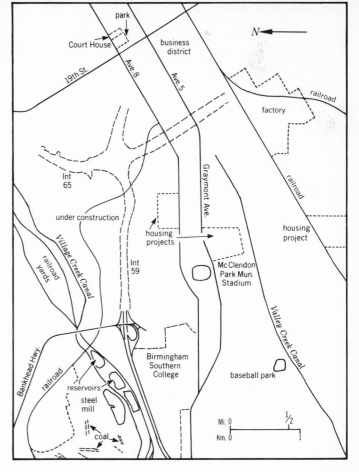

35

In this oblique view, to the horizon, of the Gulf Coast plain some aspects of the gradual seaward movement of the shoreline are visible. The bayous and delta lakes of the land-sea margin are slowly filling in. In the center of the photograph the lengthy Mississippi River delta juts out into the Gulf of Mexico. It is a characteristic bird's-foot or lobate delta fanning simultaneously in thin tendrils.

NASA

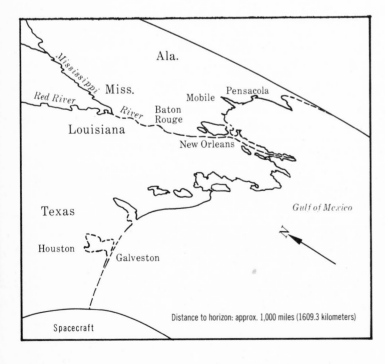

Distance to horizon: approx. 1,000 miles (1609.3 kilometers)

LOUISIANA
MISSISSIPPI

The area drained by the Mississippi River and its tributaries extends from the Great Lakes to the Gulf of Mexico, and from the Rockies of Montana to New York State.

As an agent of erosion, the river transports tremendous quantities of silt out into the Gulf of Mexico, creating new geologic formations, new land, and new structural influences as it works. One estimate of the quantity of silt so transported puts the figure at 730 thousand million tons (662 thousand million metric tons) per year. In volume this amounts to a cubic mile (4.0 cubic kilometers). Since the silt acts as a scouring agent, the river channel is cut deep, rather than filled in.

The delta of the Mississippi is a prominent landmark on any map of the United States or the

The unique location and Crescent City nickname for New Orleans are striking features of this Apollo 7 photograph. Lake Pontchartrain is a shallow delta lake whose former shoreline indicates the extent to which it has filled in. All the land in the photograph is composed of silt brought down by the river.

NASA

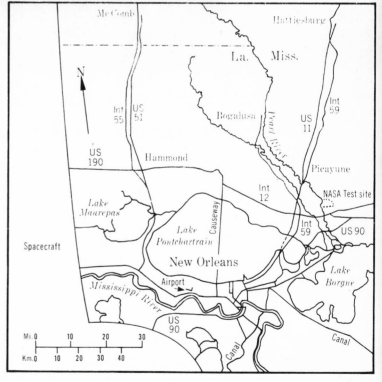

Gulf of Mexico. River-borne deposits are constantly lengthening the delta at the rate of over 250 feet (76.2 meters) per year. The extent to which the delta has grown seaward has been determined by drilling. Submarine geologists and petroleum geologists describe the underwater part of the delta to be more than 2,000 feet (610 meters) thick, extending as a wide, hummocky cone nearly 100 miles (160.9 kilometers) out into the Gulf.

Deep in the sediments of the river lie pools of petroleum trapped when impervious layers form cups or arches. Drilling for oil from offshore platforms in the shallow waters of the Gulf is a major industry of Louisiana. Inland, much older deltaic deposits include oil and natural-gas well sites.

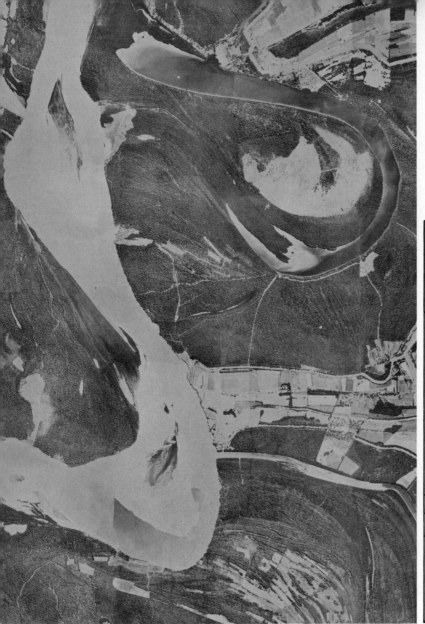

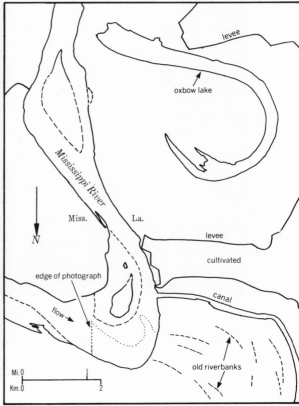

In the abstract pattern of this section of the Mississippi River and its former courses, part of the life history of the river can be read. Some of the farmland in this aerial mosaic is flooded during highwater as a flood-control safety valve. The prominent oxbow lake is a meander cut off by a change in the river's course. *SCS-USDA*

Tensas Parish, Louisiana

In its lower reaches the Mississippi River follows the classic pattern of a meandering river, cutting into its own delta and widening the river valley with great looping bends.

All rivers wind from side to side, following definite physical principles, except where resistant rock or man-made channels force the waterway into a specific course. This sinuous oscillation is called a traveling wave form, and the bends, or "wave crests," migrate downstream at a theoretically calculable rate.

As a river flows downstream, it erodes the outside banks of its bends while building up deposits on the inside edges. In a meandering river this process often goes to the extreme of creating an oblate loop. When the river cuts through the thin neck between bends, the remnant loop is dammed by silt to form an oxbow lake. With no outlet, the oxbow lake finally is filled by soil eroded from the land around it.

In the accompanying photomosaic, a large oxbow lake and the old river channels, traceable by the pattern of vegetation, are visible.

TENNESSEE

Memphis

Memphis is about three-quarters of the way from the Gulf of Mexico on a great geologic sub-surface feature called the Mississippi Embayment. The embayment is a tonguelike incursion into the continental mass of 225-million-year-old rock. It begins about 3,280 feet (1,000 meters) below the surface at Memphis, and reaches a thickness of over 6,560 feet (2,000 meters).

Overlying this basement rock east of the city are sedimentary deposits 70 million years old, with sedimentary rock laid down from about two or three million years ago across the river. The city's water supply comes not from the river but from underground where a 500-foot (152.4-meter)-thick aquifer, or water-laden sand, lies between two impermeable rock beds. This rock-sandwich stores, filters, and protects the water supply from contamination.

As it passes Memphis, the meandering course of the Mississippi River is contained somewhat by bluffs along the bank. The city itself is protected by a levee. Laid out in 1819, Memphis is one of several large cities that have always used the river as a trade route. In recent years a dam built at the upstream end of the President's Island cutoff created the only stillwater anchorage on the river. The adjacent industrial park and warehouse area are also visible in this aerial mosaic.

SCS-USDA

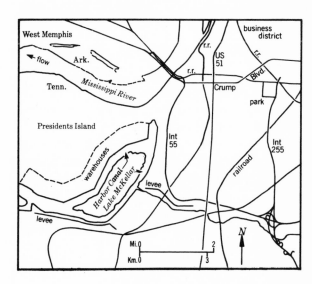

LAKE
HURON

LAKE
MICHIGAN

LAKE
ERIE

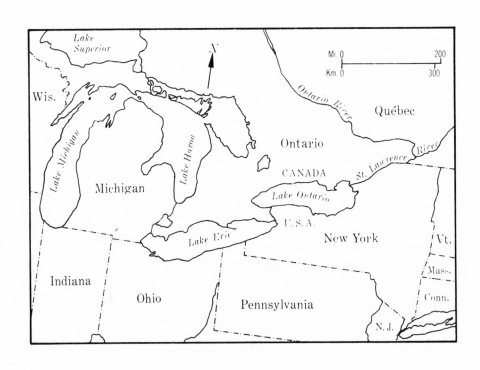

The Great Lakes

Seen as a whole, the interconnections of the Great Lakes suggest a common origin. This common point is in their formation as part of successive periods of continental glaciation and melting called the Pleistocene Ice Ages.

About 6 million square miles (15.5 million square kilometers) of Canada and the United States (including Alaska) were covered by great ice sheets at one time or another. The first advance of the ice reached its peak about 600,000 years ago, and the most recent occurred about 11,000 years ago. This later period was well within the history of man in North America.

At its maximum, the ice was 8,000 feet (2,438 meters) or more thick, with the leading edge about 2,000 feet (609.6 meters) high. The tremendous weight of the ice depressed the crust of the earth beneath it over 2,000 feet (609.6 meters) where the ice was thickest. When the ice retreated faster than the land rebounded, the ancestral Great Lakes formed in the depression on the glacial margins. Later glaciations gouged out the lake basins as meltwater of interglacial periods raised the water level, shifting the lakes' outlets. During one retreat of the ice, Lake Superior drained into the Mississippi River via Duluth, Minnesota, while Lakes Michigan and Huron had the Chicago River as their common outlet. Water from Lakes Erie and Ontario flowed through the Mohawk Valley of New York State into the Hudson River. At other times the lakes' outlets were the Saint Lawrence River (as today), the Ontario River, the Finger Lakes, and the Susquehanna River.

The earth's crust around and under the Great Lakes is still rebounding. The northern shore of Lake Superior is rising at the rate of about 20 inches (50.8 centimeters) per century. If this rate continues, Lake Michigan will again drain into the Mississippi via the Chicago River in about 1,500 years.

Geologists consider the present time as an interglacial period because the time since the last glaciation is so short compared to the 1,800,000 years since the start of the Ice Ages. Furthermore, the reasons why ice ages occur at all are unclear. Geologic evidence of other glaciation, as long as 2,600 million years and with no connection with the Pleistocene epoch, has been discovered, offering some scientific clues to a force with a very profound effect on mankind.

The glacier-born Great Lakes and their present outlet via the Saint Lawrence River dominate the geography of eight states and several provinces. Together the lakes are the largest body of fresh water in the world. With their interconnecting waterways they form the world's largest inland water-transportation unit. These overlapping photographs were taken by the Automatic Picture Transmission unit of the Nimbus 1 satellite.

NASA

MICHIGAN

Detroit

These and the following pages show aerial views of several American cities and offer a series of studies in urban development. Detroit, like many communities in the United States and Canada, began as a trading post on a waterway, and burgeoned into a rough semicircle around the original site before a great expansion in the late nineteenth and the twentieth centuries.

The principal breaks in the gridiron street plan are railroads and the industries they serve. In the past decade the Interstate Highway System has established a new pattern, with the end result not yet in sight.

A variety of contrasts lie in the small blocks of the business sections, older suburbs with tree-lined streets, and newer suburbs with irregular street layouts.

In this aerial mosaic of southeastern Detroit, a mingling of commercial and residential areas is apparent. The busy Detroit River and complex railroad system serve the automobile industry and other manufacturing concerns. Photographs of urban areas have a variety of uses for city planners, highway engineers, municipal tax departments, and service agencies.

ASCS-USDA

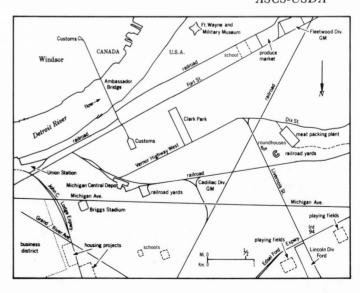

42

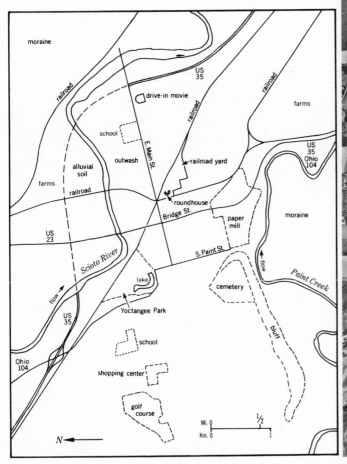

Chillicothe was one of the first permanent communities in Ohio. Emigrants from New England settled here on an old north-south Indian path, and quickly established the town as a junction with east-west routes into the Old Northwest Territory. The Scioto River originally drained part of the glacial ice sheet.

ASCS-USDA

OHIO

Chillicothe

The surface geology around Chillicothe is a mixture of glacially caused features. About 330 thousand years ago, the third of four continental glaciations bulldozed hummocks of silt and gravel, called end moraines, which straddle the city site. Melting ice formed the Scioto River, which cut through the moraine and deposited beds of sand and gravel. At the end of the last glaciation, about 11,000 years ago, the Scioto again became a meltwater channel and laid down new outwash beds — of considerable economic value today.

Historically, Chillicothe lay at a crossroads of Indian paths and eighteenth- and early-nineteenth-century wilderness roads, and was the capital of the Old Northwest Territory. The city was also the first capital of Ohio.

MISSOURI

St. Louis

Still a supersize "trading post" on the Mississippi River, St. Louis is almost an archetype of American city development. From a trading post during French occupation of the valley, it grew to become the "Gateway to the West" it proudly calls itself; it became a manufacturing center; host to the world at a great Exposition in 1904; declined economically during the mid-twentieth century; and is now experiencing urban renewal as it is rejuvenated.

Lying just south of the confluence of the Mississippi and Missouri rivers, St. Louis is the busiest port on the rivers outside deepwater Baton Rouge and New Orleans. Powerful rivercraft still called towboats now push strings of barges up and downstream, making the Mississippi from St. Louis south the most heavily traveled river in the world.

The Eads Bridge, the first steel-truss bridge in the world (built 1867-1874), is now a National Landmark. It still carries freight west in exchange for agricultural and manufactured products coming east from the vast continental interior.

The area now drained by the rivers forming the Missouri-Mississippi system was once a great shallow sea covering a much older plain. From about 320 to 185 million years ago, sediments brought in by marine waters settled gently to become packed into great beds of sedimentary rock. The outline of the sea changed as basins sank and other areas rose through uplift. Previously, about 360 to 320 million years ago, the Ozark Plateau southwest of St. Louis was raised into a dome, while to the northeast the Illinois Basin was lowered and filled with sediment. During changing patterns caused by glaciation to the north, the Mississippi was moved into its present course in a trough between the front of the glacier and the edge of the plateau. St. Louis lies in a kind of pocket between two geomorphological provinces.

St. Louis, a city in rebirth, is shown in this aerial mosaic. The areas of vacant land, once substandard housing, are now covered with new buildings, public facilities, and highways. This photograph was made before the waterfront Jefferson Memorial Arch and other ambitious projects were undertaken. The Mississippi River and railroad complex have been joined by the highways in an improved transportation network.

ASCS-USDA

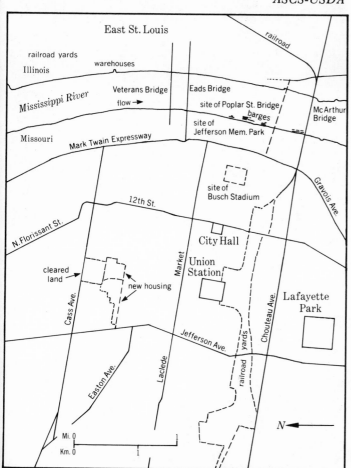

OKLAHOMA

Oklahoma City

Interpretation of the accompanying aerial photo-mosaic stresses the value of aerial photography in a variety of scientific and technical efforts. The most prominent feature is the overall grid pattern of roads and farm fields used for the township and section system of land division. In this pattern used throughout the western United States and Canada, townships are laid out in 6-mile (15.54-kilometer) squares with 1 mile (2.59 kilometer) squares called sections, the major subdivision.

Older communities further divide the sections by using a gridiron street plan. Recent urban planning concepts are apparent in those areas with irregular street patterns which were designed to relieve the monotony of the grid and for better control of traffic flow.

The impact of the region's oil industry is evident in land pockmarked by well sites and storage reservoirs. In agricultural areas, contrasting gray tones indicate different types of soil condition and a variety of crops. Vegetation along the tributaries of the North Canadian River define the treelike drainage pattern geologists call "dendritic." The main valley of the North Canadian is defined by the arcs of old meanders and subsurface soil patterns of old river deposits. These are often invisible on the ground, but when planted, tend subtly to influence crop growth in patterns recognizable from the air.

Oklahoma City's geologic location is unique. The city sits atop the confluence of six major structural elements, either arches of sedimentary rock or subsurface mountains. One of the arches slopes down to form an underground sediment-filled trough over 20,000 feet (6,096 meters) deep. At various levels, sometimes overlapping, throughout the arches and troughs, oil-and gas-bearing sands and pools form what professional geologists term "giant" petroleum reservoirs.

The search for oil has proved a boon to geology. Hollow drill bits extract cores of tremendous length as they cut through the rock. The cores provide direct measurement of each layer of strata as well as raw material for analysis. From tiny fossils in the sedimentary strata, geologists can detect ancient climates, whether the deposits were made in salt or fresh water, and even the direction of the North Magnetic Pole in eons past, before the continents assumed their present positions.

Oil, cattle, dairy farms, and extremely rapid metropolitan development characterize Oklahoma City. This aerial mosaic of the southeast section of the city shows the early section-township land pattern overlain with the curves of recent suburban developments. Eighty years ago, if a photograph had been taken of the same area, a few Indian farm buildings would have been the only structures.

SCS-USDA

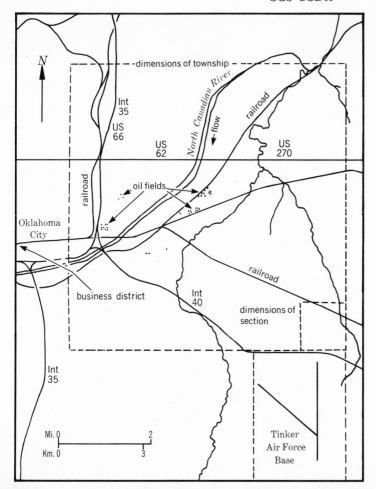

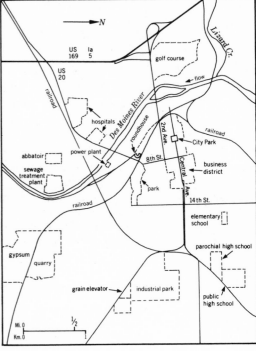

Life in prairie settlements like Fort Dodge was once deemed homespun compared to that in the great urban centers. Today, advances in technology, communications, and transportation have created new links with all sections of the country. The gypsum beds at Fort Dodge go to make wallboard for apartment houses and homes. The shopping plazas, highway interchanges, and suburban street layouts are similar to those found in every other state.

ASCS-USDA

IOWA

Fort Dodge

In glaciated sections of North American prairies, the soil cover is often the most distinctive evidence of the Ice Ages. Called glacial till, the soil is gravelly with a mixture of pebbles of obviously different origin. The weathering of the gravel indicates its origin in glacially fed streams or preglacier streams.

Although the till is not stratified, geologic cores from prairie soil show a sequence of deposition. When marine deposits or nonglacial material is encountered, some dimension of glacial action is revealed. At Fort Dodge, the glacial sequence ends with the great gypsum beds underlying the area. Gypsum is a mineral combination of calcium and sulfur precipitated on the shores of a shallow sea in an arid climate.

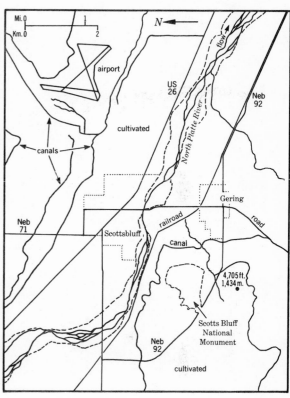

Scotts Bluff, an eroded sandstone plateau near the town of Scottsbluff, has been a landmark on the way west for nearly 140 years. Some of the emigrants on the Oregon Trail, which passes the town, stayed to develop the fertile lands of the high plains. For the past seventy years irrigation has watered the alfalfa, sugar, beet, corn, and bean crop of the region. This varied planting is apparent from the patterned fields in the aerial mosaic.

SCS-USDA

NEBRASKA

Scottsbluff

High above the western edge of the Great Plains, the eroded peaks of Scotts Bluff, and Chimney Rock nearby, were landmarks on the Oregon and Mormon trails. The peaks are resistant remnants of sandstone beds interleaved with some lava and compressed ash laid down about 25 million years ago.

Cutting down past the cliffs is the North Platte River, one of the few braided-type rivers of any size on the Plains. Essentially, this river type is a series of overlapping meanders whose physical requirements are a steeper gradient or greater discharge than that found in meandering rivers; also in a braided-type river both banks are eroded at the same time, whereas they are cut cut away only on the outside of its bends by a meandering river.

49

WYOMING

Devils Tower National Monument

In the northeastern corner of Wyoming, Devils Tower stands as a natural monument to the powers of erosion and man's fascination with the landforms of the earth. President Theodore Roosevelt, keenly aware of the natural features he saw on his visits to the West, established Devils Tower as the first National Monument in 1906. There are now more than eighty National Monuments.

Physically, the Tower stands about 600 feet (182.9 meters) above its base; which has a diameter of about 800 feet (243.8 meters). The top of the Tower is an almost flat oval about 180 feet (54.8 meters) by about 300 feet (91.4 meters). Impressive as its size is, the most striking feature of its appearance is the columns of which the Tower is formed. These are so regular that the huge rock almost appears to be a constructed edifice. The columns are polygons with four, five, or six sides up to 8 feet (2.44 meters) in diameter. They taper to about half their base dimension.

Although geologists are not in complete agreement by which geologic process the Tower was formed, they all state that it is of once-molten material that forced its way up into the sandstone and shale sedimentary beds of the area and cooled into the columnar pattern. Some geologists feel that the Tower is the remnant neck of a volcano. Recent studies indicate it is probably a once-underground intrusive body, always of about its present size, and connected, well below the surface, to other intrusive material a short distance away.

What is now Devils Tower was intruded about 70 million years ago, when the neighboring Black Hills were uplifted. Geologists call the movement of land in this area on the edge of the Rockies and the Plains the Laramide Orogeny. This Laramide movement is detectable in the structural tendencies of the front edge of the Rockies from Canada, across the United States, and well into Mexico.

The dramatic effect of erosion is evident in this aerial photograph of Devils Tower. The Tower is an intrusive body of once liquid rock that pushed up into sedimentary beds below the ground. The weaker beds have been washed away, leaving the more resistant Tower high above the plain.

USFS-USDA

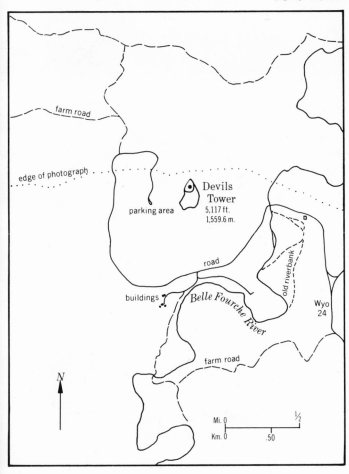

COLORADO

Rocky Mountain National Park

Like a great wall, the Front Range of the Rocky Mountains rises abruptly from the high plains of central Colorado. To early explorers and trappers, these tree-covered slopes were "rocky" in contrast to the lower, smoother Appalachians.

The tectonic, or structural, features of the Rockies in Colorado are so complex that the Rocky Mountains are a geographical feature rather than a geological unit. In between the

Longs Peak, highest in Rocky Mountain National Park, is surrounded by glacier-cut valleys and cirques. Some snow is still visible on the ground in this aerial mosaic taken during summer. Above the treeline the ground is tundra, with low grasses, flowers, and moss. The climate on the peaks is of the Arctic-Alpine type.

USFS-USDA

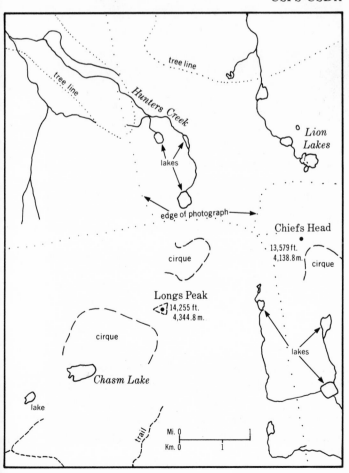

several ranges lie elevated basins locally called "parks."

The present Rockies are the third in a series of ranges to appear in this section of the continent. The Ancestral Rockies were low hills on plains. About 280 million years ago the sea rolled in for a second time; sediments were laid down to harden into rock, and the region was uplifted. As the second set of mountains was cut from the sedimentary rock, the sea again intruded to lay down layers of sediment about 10,000 feet (3,048 meters) thick.

About 70 million years ago the present Rockies began to form as a broad low arch about 50 miles (80.4 kilometers) across. As the crustal rock pushed the bulge higher, it was also being eroded. Here and there small volcanoes spewed lava over the surface. Ultimately there was formed a topography we would recognize as being similar to that of today's. The Rockies are still being uplifted.

An interval of separate but important erosion came during the Ice Ages, when this elevated region was cold enough to sustain glaciers. Evidence of glacial action is found in the cirques of the park. These amphitheatre valleys are sites of the heads of glaciers. Ice in cracks in the rock broke loose material from the sides of the cirque and enlarged it. When the ice melted, a kind of mold of its shape remained.

Since the glaciers of the Rockies were localized, they were not overly destructive of older geological features, and remnants of ancient plains and lava flows are still visible in the park. The triangular-shaped platform of Longs Peak may be a survivor of one of these old plains. Buried for millions of years beneath deep sediments, it was finally exposed by eons of erosion. A geologist once wrote that the record of the rocks is like a mutilated and badly printed book with pages missing, un-numbered, or out of sequence. From this material geologists have patiently assembled a solidly based chronology of geologic events.

53

To the airborne traveler views of remote terrain, such as the Dirty Devil River in Utah shown in this photograph, are one of the assets of flying. The river is flowing toward the camera, as evidenced by the gravel buildup on the outside curves and lack of it on the inside curves. To the right, highly eroded rock knobs indicate ancient rapids.

Kenneth L. Fitzgerald

UTAH

In the arid landscape of the western states, geologic features are not concealed by vegetation. Former river channels, ancient rapids, differing rates of erosion, and the power of meandering rivers are in plain view. Incisive meanders, cut deep into sedimentary layers, are called "entrenched meanders." When they finally cut through the meander neck, a tunnel is sometimes formed. Later, wind and water erosion whittle away the surrounding rock as the old meander dries up in the desert heat. The end result is sometimes one of the spectacular natural bridges of the West.

The accompanying photograph shows the potential for amateur aerial photography from commercial airline flights. Film manufacturers publish booklets detailing filter and shutter-speed requirements for the airborne tourist photographer.

54

In their efforts to analyze the surface of our planet, scientists continually seek new methods of gathering information. This photograph is a black-and-white version of a near-infrared sensitive print. The original was taken from an altitude of 200,000 feet (60.9 kilometers) by an X-15 aircraft. Since the film was sensitive only to the deeply penetrating near-infrared radiation, their reflection was caught by the camera, and especially emphasizes geologic and land-use characteristics.

NASA

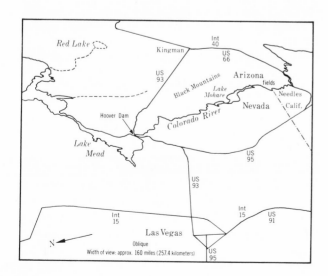

NEVADA

Near Las Vegas a great bend in the Colorado River shows the power of rock structure to determine a river's general trend. To the east, the Colorado flows through the elevated Colorado Plateau, southwest of the Rocky Mountains. At Lake Mead the river cuts across the Basin and Range physiographic province of Nevada and Arizona, whose mountains are formed of great fractured blocks of rock towering above arid valleys filled with material eroded off the rugged slopes. An excellent view of this topography is in the astronaut photograph of the Salton Sea in this atlas.

Lake Mead was created when Hoover Dam was finished in 1936. Water in the lake weighs 12 million tons (13.2 million metric tons) and has depressed a 30-mile (48.3-kilometer)-wide section of the earth's crust nearly 5 inches (12.7 centimeters).

Las Vegas is an excellent example of man's ability today to build large communities in remote and inhospitable deserts.

55

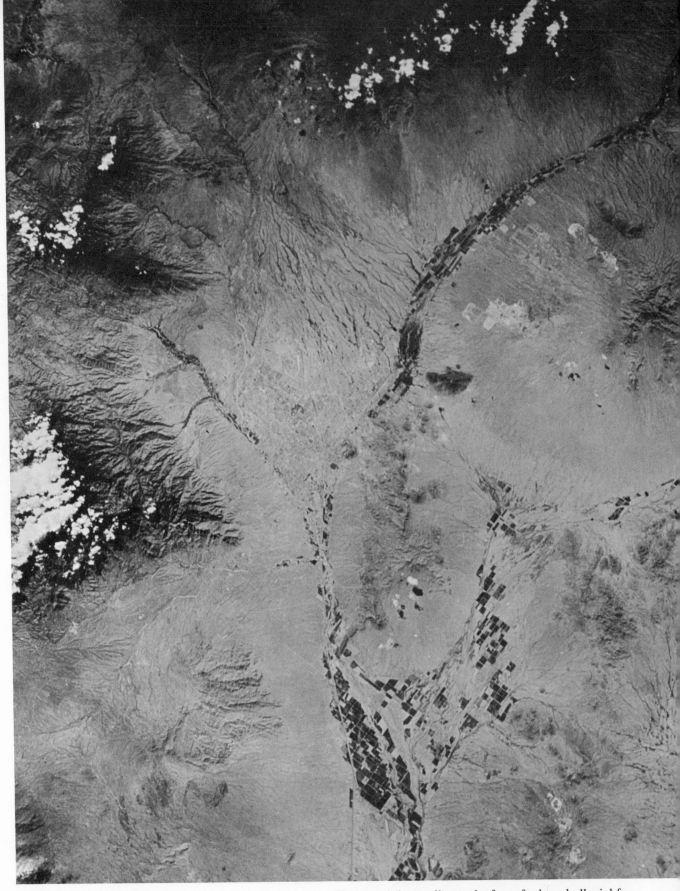

Tucson, Arizona, lies at the foot of a broad alluvial fan surrounded by nearly bare mountains of volcanic rock. Also prominent in this Gemini 5 photograph are the extensive open-pit mines of the area, the narrow agricultural belts of river bottoms, and a few small volcanic outcrops of comparatively youthful geologic age. *NASA*

ARIZONA

Southern Arizona lies in the northern part of the Sonoran Desert, named for the adjacent Mexican state of Sonora. The surface geology of the region is indicative of the arid climate as well as the complex folding with volcanic intrusions of this part of the western cordillera.

The rocks range from over-600-million-year-old metamorphic material to million-year-old volcanic peaks, with younger sediments filling the valleys. Metamorphic rocks are those altered underground by heat, pressure, and chemical reaction. Originally they may have been sedimentary or once-molten material. Underground, great quantities of valuable minerals were formed by structural changes, heat, and water.

Copper is the principal product of Arizona mines, but iron, lead, manganese, silver, and zinc are extracted in commercial quantities.

Comparison of the photographs on these pages shows the tremendous difference in scale now available in aerial photography.

In the Gemini and Apollo photographs, the urban areas appear as a mass, with detail limited to geologic trends, irrigated areas, and large

East of Tucson lies Willcox Dry Lake, a large playa. In this Apollo 6 photograph, taken during the spring, water-soaked sand and mud in the playa are a visible result of winter runoff. Some snow remains on the higher peaks of surrounding mountains. At the bottom of the photograph a thin smoke plume locates Douglas on the Arizona-Sonora state, Mexico, border.   *NASA*

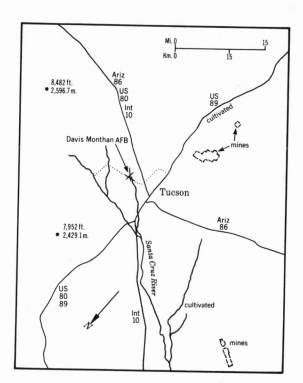

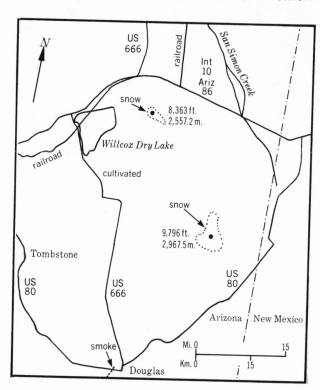

This panoramic view of part of the Fort Huachuca Proving Grounds shows the great detail possible using modern aerial techniques. Reproduced the same size as the original, in the photograph the resolution target (see accompanying enlargement) is barely discernible. Yet lines only 3 inches (7.6 centimeters) in width can be seen in the original. The photo was made from 18,000 feet (5,486.4 meters) by a camera using a rotating lens.

Fairchild Space and Defense Systems

man-made features. In the panoramic aerial photograph of part of Fort Huachuca, buildings, houses, and even individual fence posts can be seen. Both types of pictures have considerable value in a variety of science and engineering disciplines.

Analyses of geologic trends and types of rock are useful to the mining engineer and the geologist for the discovery of mineral resources and the evolution of landforms. To the agricultural expert, crop analysis, potential farm-or grazing land, and calculation of acreage currently under the plow, as well as other factors, can be quickly determined from aerial and space photographs.

Urban planners, municipal departments, and other governmental agencies increasingly find aerial photographs the fastest method of gathering statistics for such diverse purposes as tax studies, land use, water use, regional planning, and recreation-area investigations. The value of aerial photographs is in their overall view, their accuracy for measurement, and their exact depiction of the ground. The information displayed in a single aerial photograph would take a tremendous number of man-hours to gather on the ground.

The value of thousands of Gemini and Apollo aerial photographs is such that the National Academy of Sciences, National Research Council, and the House of Representatives Subcommittee on Space Science and Applications have urged NASA to put an Earth Resources Technology Satellite into orbit. The ERTS program would cover agriculture, forestry, geology, geodesy, oceanography, fisheries, and hydrology as the chief interests.

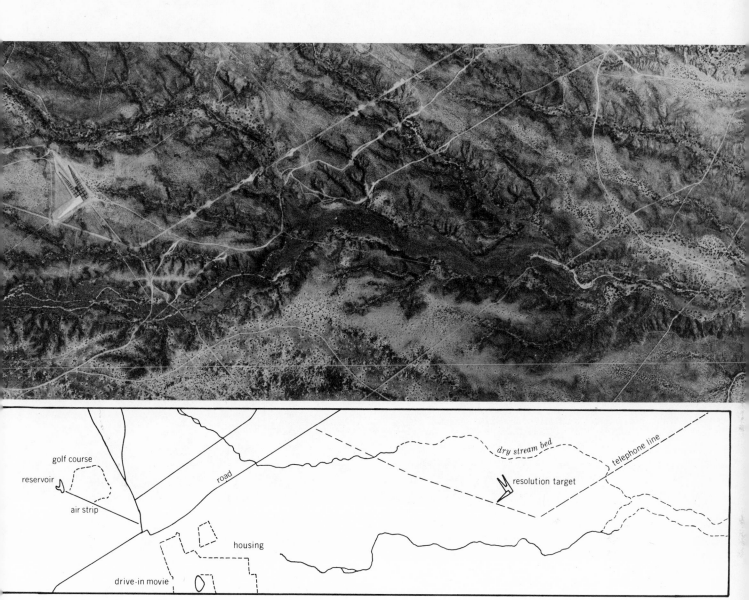

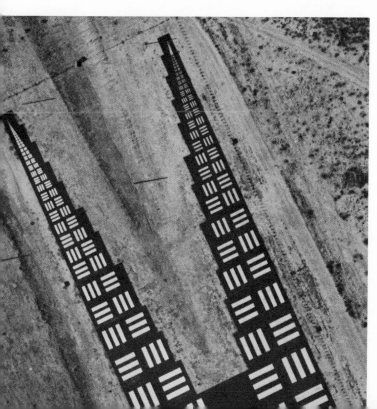

Features as small as fence posts can be seen in this enlargement of part of the resolution target section of the strip panoramic view above.

Fairchild Space and Defense Systems

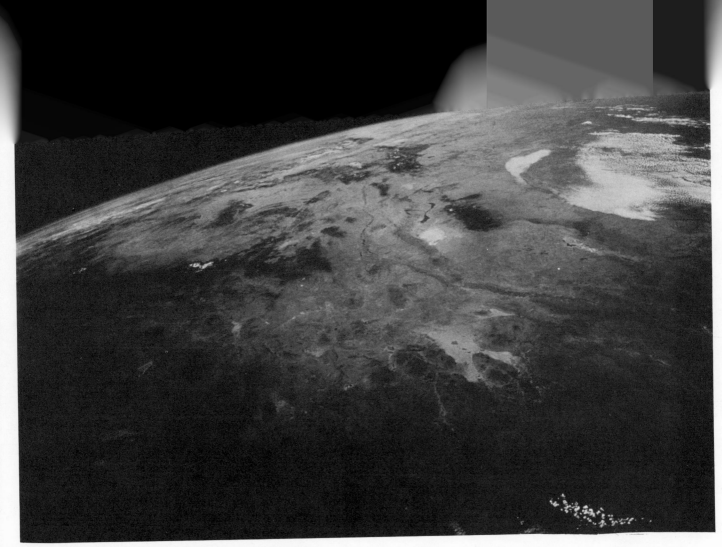

Most of New Mexico and part of west Texas is covered in this Gemini 12 photograph. Some of the dark-colored mountain peaks are outcrops of volcanic rock; others are tree-covered remnants of sedimentary layers filling great underground basins. To the far right, clouds cover the western edge of the Great Plains.

NASA

Distance to horizon: approx. 1,000 miles (1609.3 kilometers)

Rocky Mountains

Kansas

Denver Colorado

Utah

Albuquerque

Oklahoma

Pecos River

New Mexico White Sands

playa

El Paso

Texas

Flagstaff Gila River

Rio Grande

Arizona

Tucson Willcox Dry Lake

Laguna de Santa Maria
(dry lake)

N

MEXICO

NEW MEXICO

In central New Mexico the Río Grande valley is a "graben," or depressed structural block with faults on opposite sides. The region is also one of lava beds and mountains of volcanic rock.

Many geological and geographical terms for features in the Southwest are those first applied by Spanish explorers. A "playa," for example, is a dry lake bed in the lowest part of a "bolson" (purse), which is an enclosed valley. The spare rainfall drains down canyons and arroyos, at whose mouths lie "bajada" (gradual descent), which are overlapping alluvial fans of eroded silt.

The Rio Grande (Rio Grande del Norte, or Río Bravo, in Mexico) irrigates an important agricultural section of New Mexico.

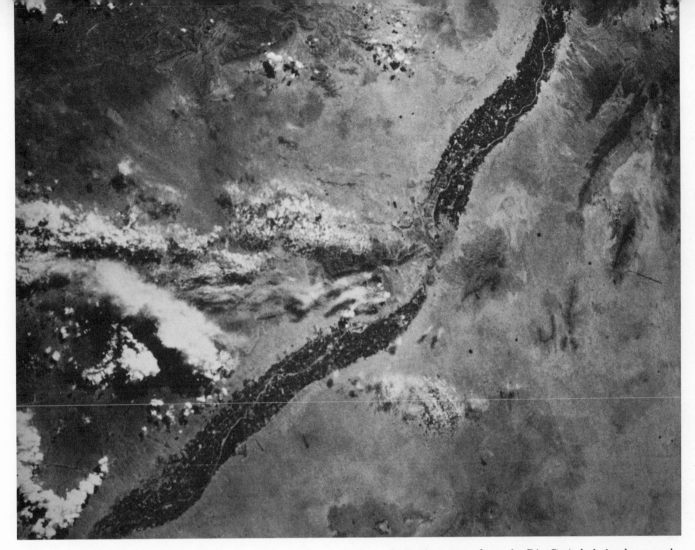

Irrigation water from the Rio Grande helped create the checkerboard pattern of fields in the river valley. El Paso and Juárez lie at the end of the Franklin Mountains and break the agricultural pattern. The fertility of the desert soil is apparent in the many farms, but equally as striking is the importance of water in this arid climate.

NASA

TEXAS

El Paso

Irrigation in the Rio Grande Valley is so intense that in aerial photographs the watered fields stand out in sharp contrast to the surrounding desert. At El Paso the river provides a travel route through the Franklin Mountains. This short range of folded sedimentary rock was formed between 350 and 225 million years ago and was later disturbed by lava flows. Kilbourne Hole nearby is a "maar," or explosive volcano, now extinct.

The region around El Paso marks a geologic transition zone between the faulted blocks of the southern Rockies and the folded ranges of Mexico.

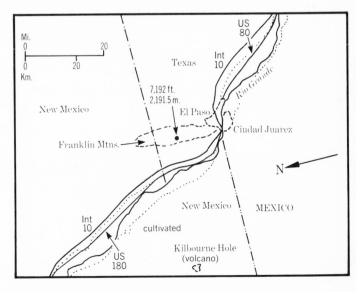

In western Texas, oil-laden sediments lie at various depths, but the original strikes were made in sands of the Permian geologic epoch. The name survives in company names and in the geographical Permian Basin, shown in this Gemini 4 photograph. To the left is a darkened tongue of ground, soaked by rain the day before the photograph was taken.

NASA

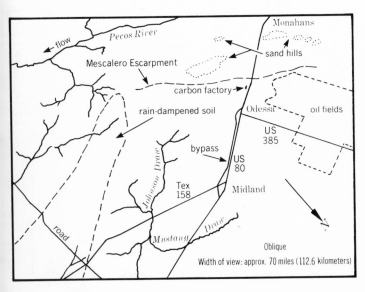

Midland

Odessa

From the Texas–New Mexico border to the Rio Grande lie more than 10,000 feet (3,048 meters) of layered limestone, sandstone, shale, and salt that form the oil-rich region known as the Permian Basin. Midland lies near the western edge of the subsidiary Midland Basin, which extends east and north under the Staked Plain (Llano Estacado). The Mescalero Escarpment marks the western edge of the Plains.

Investigation in West Texas and elsewhere has given scanty clues as to the basic origin of petroleum. The strongest scientific evidence thus far suggests that it is an organic compound derived from a chemical breaking down of microscopic plants and animals, possibly living under tidewater conditions.

To Texans the state is divided into two principal parts: East and West, with the Panhandle and lower Rio Grande Valley as adjuncts. In the Rio Grande Valley, Uvalde represents traditional Texas, surrounded by cattle ranches and pecan groves in what was the original home of the famous longhorn cattle.

NASA

Uvalde

One of the experiments conducted during the Gemini 5 flight was a visual acuity test based on a ground pattern laid out in southern Texas. Although the accompanying photograph shows the pattern, the several processes involved between the original film and the printed page have resulted in some loss of quality.

Each of the dark squares is a 2,000-foot square (185.8 square meters) of the cleared and plowed land. On each square, large patterns were made from sheets of white wallboard. The astronauts on the flight were Gordon Cooper and Charles Conrad. Colonel Cooper was chosen for the test because during his Mercury 9 flight he described ground detail theoretically impossible to see from his orbital altitude. The tests and later flights showed the view from space to be more detailed than previously thought.

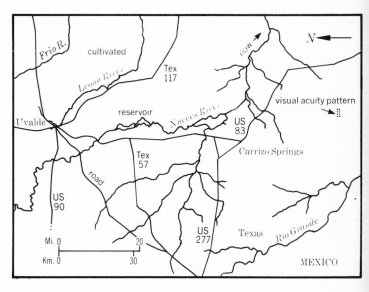

Dallas

Fort Worth

The size of the Dallas-Fort Worth megalopolis is one of the striking features in the above photo-montage. The two overlapping photographs were taken during the Apollo 6 mission and cover a 150-mile-wide (241.4-kilometer) section of north-central Texas.

General geographic features, such as the meandering rivers of the prairie, major highways, numerous reservoirs, and acreage under cultivation, are prominent even from the 138-statute-mile altitude at which the photographs were taken. The tonal contrast in farm areas is owing to the colors of different crops and to the fact that the photographs were taken in the spring.

The Interstate Highway ring around Dallas and the roads radiating from the urban core are similar in plan to the road and street system of medieval towns, with the ring resembling the road around an old town wall.

During the latter half of the nineteenth century, Fort Worth was a cattle and meat-packing center, but Dallas developed as a cotton-market town. As the photographs show, open rangeland has almost vanished as the urban areas have grown. This urbanization is indicative of the cities' present economic base as the scientific, commercial, industrial, and cultural centers of east Texas.

Fort Worth, Dallas, and more than 11,000 square miles (28,490 square kilometers) of north-central Texas are shown in this overlapping pair of photographs. The pictures were made by automatic cameras aboard the unmanned Apollo 6 flight. Geographically the area shown in the left photograph is of a slightly different climatic, topographic, and soil type from the Fort Worth-Dallas region. The most striking differences between the photographs are in the megalopolis of Fort Worth-Dallas, the meandering course of rivers, and light-colored crops of extensive farmlands to the left.

NASA

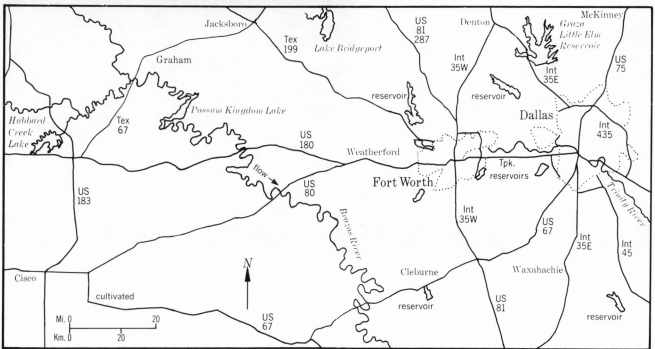

Houston

One useful result from Gemini spaceflight photography was the discovery that such pictures are of value to oceanography. The accompanying Gemini 12 photograph of the Texas-Louisiana coast, for example, shows a number of phenomena of interest to an oceanographic photo-interpreter.

Coastal oceanography is particularly concerned with the relationship between the sea and land. In essence, the land is static and the waves and currents are forces reshaping it. The accompanying photograph shows sediments being borne by the tide out of Galveston Bay and Sabine Lake. At the time the picture was taken, the Houston Ship Channel was being redredged. The channel itself is visible as a dark line in the shallow waters of the bay. In the upper bay, dredged material dumped on the edge of the channel is seen as a light-colored line.

Some of the sediment being borne out of the bay and along the shore is a result of dredging operations that loosened slightly consolidated material. The general distribution of material outward is offset by sand being carried into bays and estuaries and silt flowing downriver from the land. Long-term photography of a bay, using dye markers to study currents and waves, may enable oceanographers to forecast sections of the shore destined for erosion so that preventitive measures can begin while the attack is yet in its early stages.

The area shown in the photograph is some of the best shrimp-fishing ground in the world. Shrimp move into the tidal estuaries in an early stage of their lives, and return to the sea as adults. Accurate knowledge of sea conditions can be used to predict stages of the shrimp life cycle and, therefore, fishing possibilities.

Farther out to sea and in other areas of the world, tuna, herring, and anchovies are types of fish that live in specific water conditions, moving in schools to find their best habitats. Space photography of changing sea conditions would enable fishermen to determine the best fishing grounds.

As a city, Houston has figured prominently in Texas affairs since its founding in 1836 as the then capital of the Texas Republic and as a prosperous railroad and shipping center. Now, as the home of the Manned Spacecraft Center, it has attracted a number of aerospace firms to the area.

Some indication of the value of aerial photography from space is shown in this view of Houston, Galveston, and the Texas-Louisiana coast. From each bay mouth sediments are being carried southwesterly along the coast.

NASA

The geologic structure and basic rock types of Southern California are visible in this Gemini 5 oblique photograph. Inland, the Salton Sea shows the location of an area depressed below sea level. Offshore, the islands of Santa Catalina and San Clemente are the peaks of mountains under the sea less than ten thousand years ago.

NASA

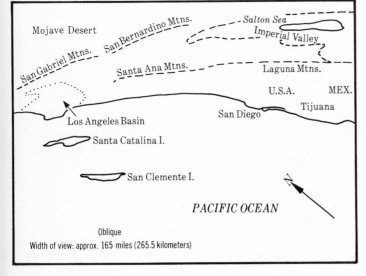

CALIFORNIA

The geologic structure of California is of the same general type but much younger than that of the East Coast of the continent; here a deep trough or geosyncline was filled with sediment and folded while being raised. This activity was accompanied by intrusions of molten material from beneath the earth's crust, volcanoes on the surface, and faulting, with considerable earthquake activity.

The comparison between East and West Coasts can only be in generalities, however. Each has been affected by local conditions and by

A closeup view of the Salton Sea and Imperial Valley taken during the Gemini 5 flight. The dark color of most of the fields is an indication that the crops are alfalfa, beans, and low-growing vegetable crops with large dark leaves. Comparison with other photographs in this atlas shows the contrast with lighter (except in spring) grain crops in the Great Plains. The reason for the current pattern in the water is unknown to professional hydrologists.

NASA

larger factors such as continental drift, the Ice Ages, and the epochs in which most of the geologic activity took place.

About 135 million years ago molten rock — "magma" — forced its way into sedimentary beds near what was then the shore of the Pacific Ocean. The magma solidified to form the granitic rocks that make up a complex rock mass, called a "batholith," that forms the core of the Sierra Nevada range. Two or three million years ago a westward tilt of a huge block of the earth's crust rapidly raised the Sierra and accelerated the process of erosion. Today much of the Sierra Nevada batholith has been laid bare, and estimates indicate that from 10 1/2 to 13 1/3 miles (17 to 22 kilometers) of rock have been eroded from atop the batholith.

South of the Sierra the granite mountains of Southern California and Baja California continue the same trend. Along the Pacific shore, the Coast Range is composed of folded marine deposits laid down between 40 to 12 million years ago; some granitic material and older deposits of the type that once covered the Sierra Nevada.

The folding, erosion, and transfer of great quantities of sediment in California was partly aided by land movements along the network of faults and fracture zones, particularly in Southern California. On a grander scale, the Salton Sea lies in the upper end of a rift, part of the globe-encircling system. Once the upper end of the Gulf of California, the Salton Sea-Imperial Valley Basin was cut off when silt from the Colorado River created a natural dam.

Until this century the basin was dry land called the Salton Sink. Then, in 1905-1907, floodwaters from the Colorado poured through a broken levee to fill the lowest, unpopulated part of the basin. The gap in the levee was closed only when the Southern Pacific Railroad dumped trainloads of boulders — cars and all — into the rushing waters.

The Salton Sea remained fresh water for a few years, but evaporation increased the salinity. In recent years drainage from irrigated farmlands in the Imperial Valley has helped maintain the lake at a nearly constant level.

Palmdale

Near the community of Palmdale, in the Antelope Valley, the famous San Andreas Fault is visible as a shallow trench about 3 miles (4.82 kilometers) wide. Comparison of the geological structure on both sides of the fault shows the amount of displacement. The San Andreas Fault is of the strike-slip type whose movement is largely horizontal. Vertical faults form cliffs of various heights called "fault scarps."

Lateral displacement along the fault, near Palmdale, has been a northward movement of about 5 miles (8.05 kilometers) on the western side. The maximum movement anywhere along the fault has been about 200 miles (321.9 kilometers).

The San Andreas Fault has been traced for 600 miles (965.6 kilometers) on land, from the Imperial Valley through San Francisco. There is strong geologic evidence that it begins in the Gulf of California sea-floor rift, crosses California, and joins an ocean-floor fracture called the Mendecino Fracture Zone, off the northern California coast, which lies at right angles to the fault.

In detail, the San Andreas Fault is a fault system with branches, cross faults, and differing rates of movement. The southern and northern sections of the fault are locked segments along which movement is very slight at present. Between the two sections is about 130 miles (209.2 kilometers) of nearly constant activity. What concerns seismologists is that the two locked sections may be under tension and could spring loose, unleashing a major earthquake. To learn more about the fault, field workers from the United States Geological Survey National Center for Earthquake Studies constantly survey the fault to measure the amount of land movement. Scientists at the ESSA Geodetic Research Laboratory have tested the use of tower-mounted aerial cameras in other areas in an attempt to photograph the extent of any small movement, with useful results.

The nearly straight line of part of the San Andreas Fault zone is especially apparent as it forms one bank of Palmdale Reservoir. The community itself lies at the edge of the nearly level Antelope Valley, and is separated from the metropolitan part of Los Angeles County by mountains.

ASCS-USDA

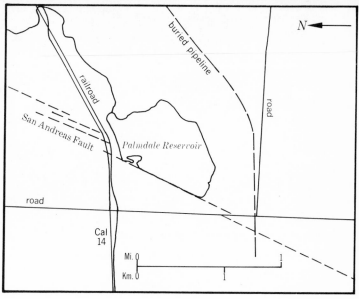

Much of the activity of the early conservation movement in the United States centered upon the establishment of the Yosemite Valley as the third national park. The valley is a glacially carved U-shape, partially filled with alluvial material eroded from higher elevations. Streams and waterfalls drain the branching, hanging valleys.

USFS-USDA

Yosemite National Park

" . . . no temple made with hands can compare to Yosemite. Every rock in its walls seems to glow with life." John Muir, the great naturalist who knew Yosemite as few other men have, thus described his feelings about this spectacular gash in the Sierra Nevada.

In opposition to some prominent professional geologists of his day, Muir declared the steep-sided Yosemite Valley to be the result of gouging by glacial action. His opposition felt the valley to be the result of some natural catastrophe.

Yosemite Valley is actually a composite valley, having passed through three major stages of

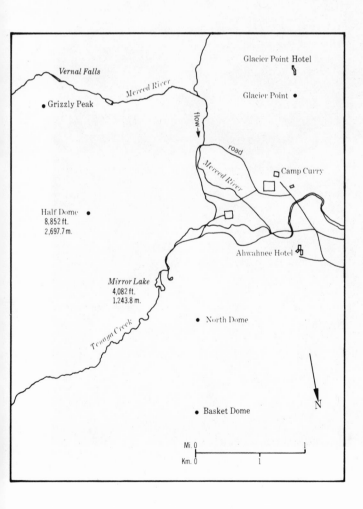

erosion. The original valley was cut by what is now the Merced River, about 70 million years ago, in the then sediment-covered Sierra Nevada, a range of low hills about 1,500 feet (457.2 meters) high. Vertical uplift, totaling 7,000 feet (2,133.6 meters) several million years ago, and a westward tilt of this section of the earth's crust forced the river to cut a narrow channel more rapidly than before.

A great glacier flowed into this second valley about one million years ago, when a colder climate prevailed because of the massive continental glaciation far to the north. The glacier gouged a wide U-shaped valley through the basic rock of the Sierra Nevada batholith. The present, or third, stage of the valley's development is one of water erosion as the Merced meanders through the valley clogged with glacial debris and silt eroded from the upper slopes.

Half Dome, one of the impressive rock features of the park, rises as a granite monolith more than 4,800 feet (1,463 meters) above the valley floor. It is being weathered on the domed side by a flaking process called "exfoliation."

The lofty tributary valleys whose streams create the valley's spectacular waterfalls are called "hanging valleys" by geologists. They were cut by small glaciers branching off the ice that created the main valley.

Yosemite became a national park in 1890 after having become a state forest reservation under an act signed by Abraham Lincoln. Frederick Law Olmsted, one of the architects of New York's Central Park, Prospect Park in Brooklyn, and Mont Royal Park in Montreal, was on the first Board of Commissioners for Yosemite. This joining of the mountains of the Far West and the eastern city parks underlies conservationists' concern for parklands.

NAPL Photo A16848-45

74

Canada

Québec

The early prominence of Québec lay in its domination of the Saint Lawrence River, as is evident in the accompanying aerial photograph. Les Plaines d'Abraham, today the Parc des Champs de Bataille, and the Citadel are historic reminders of the city's history during wars with the French and the Americans.

Below the heights, and across the river, grain-loading terminals, shipyards, and oil-storage depots testify to Québec's importance as a maritime port. Patches of snow are visible in the farm fields across the river. The linearity of the fields is reminiscent of continental practice and contrasts with the square township and section style of English Canada and the United States.

The city is a center of French Canadian culture, and the provincial capital of Québec.

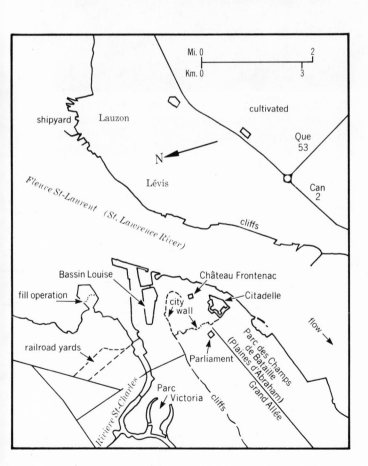

Cratère du Nouveau Québec

A dramatic instance of scientific application of aerial photography was the discovery, in 1943, of the Cratère du Nouveau Québec by the United States Air Force. Afterward, from 1955 to 1965, some two million aerial photographs of Canada were examined in a search for other craters. By 1968, fourteen other Canadian craters had been discovered on aerial photographs by technicians at the Dominion Observatory, Ottawa.

Thirteen years lapsed between the discovery and exploration of the Québec Crater. In the interim, it was known by several other names before the current official geographical name. It is still sometimes called the New Québec Crater, Chubb Crater (after a prospector who visited the site), and Ungava Crater (for the section of Québec in which it lies).

On-site examination of the 2-mile- (3.21-kilometer) wide crater, which has a 300-foot- (91.4-meter) high raised rim, definitely confirmed it to be of meteoric nature.

This Québec crater is a larger version of the Barringer Crater (also Meteor Crater) near Flagstaff, Arizona, which was the first meteor crater in the world to be identified as such. Natural scientific caution on the part of astronomers and also the fact that obviously titanic extraterrestrial forces — forces never directly observed by man — were needed to produce so large a hole made the meteor theory scarcely credible at first. Since the Barringer Crater was "accepted" in 1929, about a dozen craters all over the world have been shown to be of impact origin. About a hundred other circular disturbances of local rock have been suggested as possible craters.

Most of the problem in identifying true meteorite craters is that many of the structures are highly eroded and often resemble remnants of eroded, once-domed sedimentary rock, and are apparently formed under differing conditions. A meteor does not strike the earth like a cannonball and bury itself in the ground as a solid mass. Instead, it heats up by friction as it passes

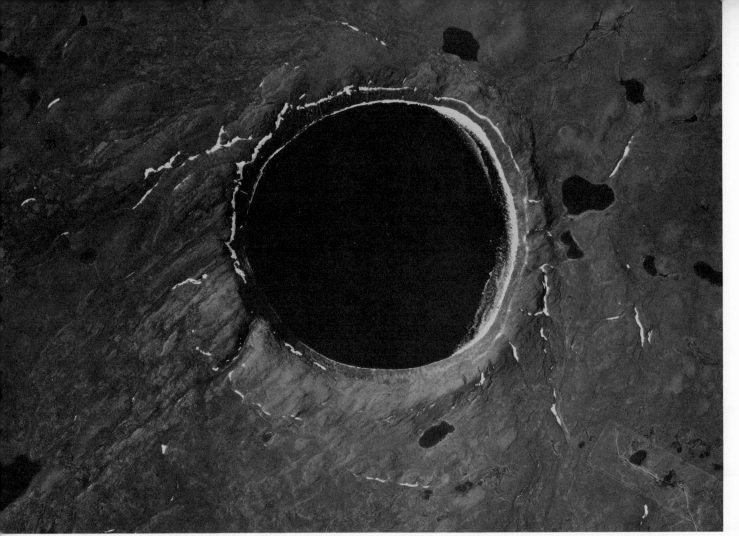

The meteorite that made this crater cut into the ancient rocks of the barren Canadian Shield. The Shield is a vast region of northeastern Canada whose exposed rocks are the foundation of the northern part of the continent.

Radiometric dating, using atom decay of minerals as a timing device, shows the rocks near the crater to be about 1,900 million years old.

NAPL Photo A1616-110

through the atmosphere, and may even disintegrate. What reaches the surface of the earth, traveling at supersonic speed, is a ball of hot gases and meteoritic material preceded by a shockwave, all of which causes an explosion when it hits.

Some circular structures are caused by comet impact. A comet has less body than a meteor and almost no residue remains, whereas a large meteor leaves thousands of meteorite fragments around the hole. Smaller meteors often survive intact.

In this atlas, a photograph of another possible meteor site, the Richat Structure, is in the section on Africa. And a comet crater, Gosses Bluff, is shown in a photograph of part of Australia.

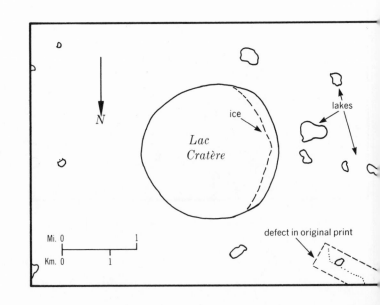

76

Industries based on the tremendous forest and water resources of Ontario and Québec lie close to the national seat of government, as this aerial photomosaic shows. The growth of the urban area is apparent in the segmented gridiron street layout. Old riverbanks and alluvial deposits show alterations in the rivers' courses.

NAPL Photos A20269-65, -66, -84, -85

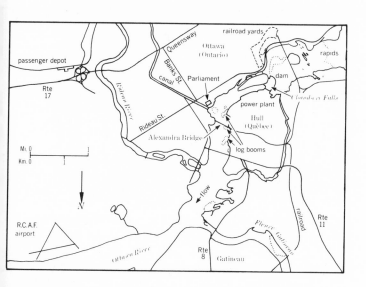

ONTARIO

Ottawa

The Canadian capital was originally settled in 1827 as construction headquarters during the building of the Rideau Canal. Using the canal and a chain of lakes and natural waterways, Royal Engineers succeeded in bypassing the narrow section of the Saint Lawrence that lies between the United States and Canada. Establishment as the capital came during the series of conferences leading to the National Confederation in 1867.

As an industrial site Ottawa has the advantage of Chandière Falls and Rideau Falls to provide hydroelectric power and an abundant supply of water. In the accompanying aerial mosaic, several mills and a number of log booms are visible. The logs are towed upriver or floated down by encircling them with a floating chain to create the boom. They are felled in the vast forests of Ontario and Québec.

About 5,000 to 4,000 years ago, the Ottawa River was the eastern outlet of Lake Huron. During this time the ice sheet was at its maximum recession, with the result that geologists call the Climatic Optimum, or Altithermal. During the Optimum, weather in the latitude of Ottawa was similar to that of the Mediterranean region today.

Although much of the area shown in the accompanying aerial mosaic has been built on, some elements of older river terraces remain. At the end of the last glaciation, this part of Canada lay under an arm of what geologists call the Champlain or Saint Lawrence Sea. This "sea" was an embayment of the St. Lawrence River valley. Its limits have been determined by marine terraces and beaches on what are now mountainsides.

The urban regions shown in the mosaic have developed in a pattern similar to other North American cities, as the photographs in other parts of this atlas show.

SASKATCHEWAN

Saskatoon

The prairie provinces of Canada owe their soil and topography to the continental ice sheet and to a long-vanished glacial lake: Lake Agassiz. Named for Louis Agassiz, a Swiss-American naturalist who developed the theory of glaciation, the lake covered at its greatest extent an area larger than the present Great Lakes combined. Saskatoon lies at what was once the bottom of a huge embayment of Lake Agassiz called Lake Regina.

At another stage of glaciation the region shown in the accompanying aerial mosaic was covered by the ice that cut the numerous vegetation-filled kettles. Beneath the surface lies part of an unexploited coal measure whose extraction is uneconomical owing to petroleum and natural-gas deposits nearby.

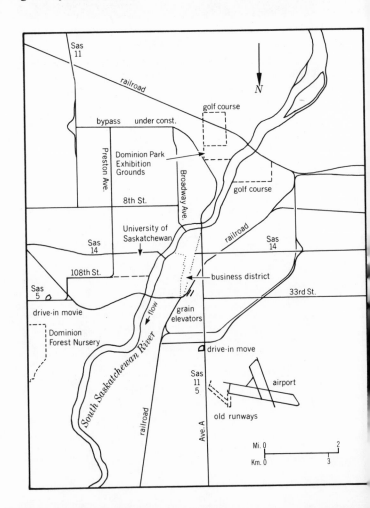

In the provinces of the interior plain, farm fields are often rectangular, in conformity with the sectional division of land. Not only is this pattern easily surveyed; it also has the advantage of simple documentation and description in deeds. The tree nurseries are part of the University of Saskatchewan's efforts to exploit the nearby forests which invaded the then treeless grassland 4,000 to 3,500 years ago.

NAPL Photos A19742-48, -49, -112, -113

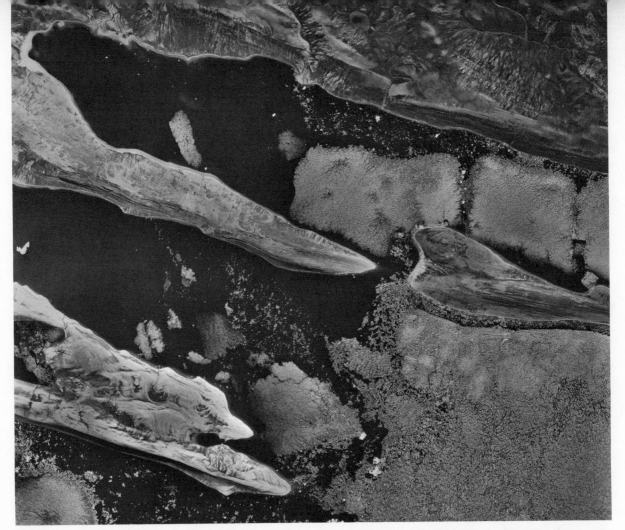

Bathurst Island in the Canadian Arctic is a desolate, ice-carved wasteland, even in summer, as this aerial photograph shows. Despite the extensive smoothing of the rock by the vanished glacial ice, some evidence that the land is made of sedimentary beds is visible on the hillsides. The broken pattern of floating ice shows it is seasonal, and not the permanent variety found in the Arctic Ocean.

NAPL Photo A16151-13

NORTHWEST TERRITORIES

Bathurst Island, District of Franklin

Ice-scarred Bathurst is one of thousands of islands in the Canadian Arctic. What makes it unique is that it has been the general geographic location of the North Magnetic Pole in recent years. The Pole itself is not a terrestrial feature but the point on the earth's surface where a freely suspended compass needle has a vertical dip of 90 degrees. The earth itself is a gigantic magnet, and a north- or south-pointing compass aligns itself with the earth's magnetic field.

Geophysicists are able to measure the "fossil" magnetism retained by rocks since their formation to determine the location of magnetic poles of the past. Their discovery that the magnetic poles have wandered over half their hemispheres also shows that the continents have moved relative to the magnetic poles — a clue to the nature of continental drift.

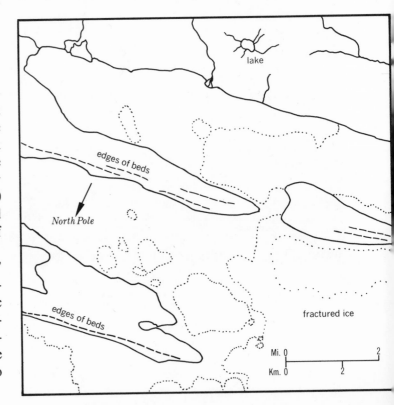

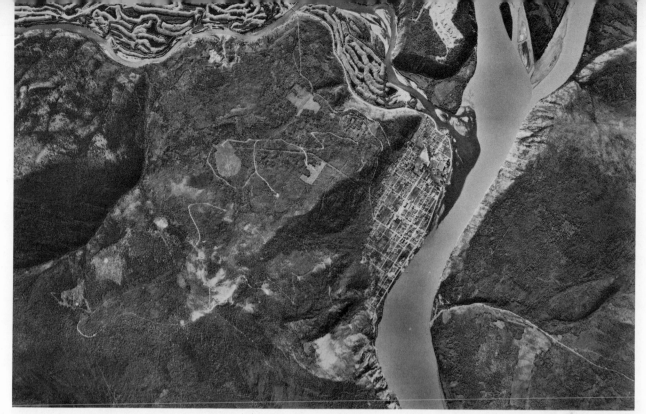

NAPL Photo A17155-55

YUKON TERRITORY

Dawson

Remnants of the Klondike Gold Rush of the late nineteenth and early twentieth centuries dominate the accompanying aerial view. The community of Dawson covers a much smaller area than the tremendous mounds of debris left by mining operations. Only a small part of the linear piles of tailings that line Klondike Creek are shown in the photograph. Their age is indicated by the fact that a road has been laid over the mounds.

Today the Creek is clear, compared to the muddy Yukon, showing that the mechanical washing of hillside gravel for gold has stopped. Tree-covered slopes smooth the contours of this part of the cordilleran belt, which is the center part of an arc joining the ranges of Alaska to the Canadian Rockies.

The chief economic activity in the region today is asbestos production, with the navigable Yukon River a transport route.

Early explorers thought Baja California was an island, and many early maps showed it as such long after the truth was known. The "island of California" was a legend written before the coast was explored, and the discovery of the peninsula lent credence to the romantic idea.

NASA

Mexico

Baja California

The rugged Baja California peninsula is a great spine of fault-cut, once-molten rock separated from mainland Mexico by the Gulf of California. The peninsula is an extension of the granite mountains of California. In 1850 Alta, or Upper, California became an American state, while Baja, or Lower, California remained a Mexican state. Today the southern half of the peninsula comprises the Territory of Baja California Sur.

Because it is so close to the research institutions of Mexico and the United States, both sections of Baja California and the Gulf are under constant study by geologists and oceanographers. Originally — and erroneously — thought to be an island by early explorers, it is now apparently becoming an island, according to scientific studies published in the summer of 1969.

Examination of the sea floor of the Gulf by instrument-laden oceanographic vessels, combined with geologic surveys on land, show that

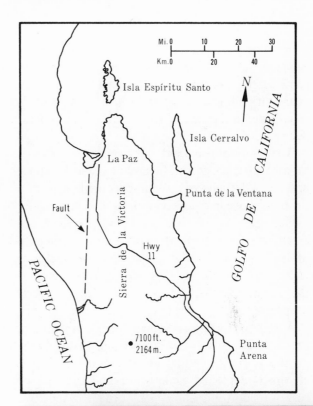

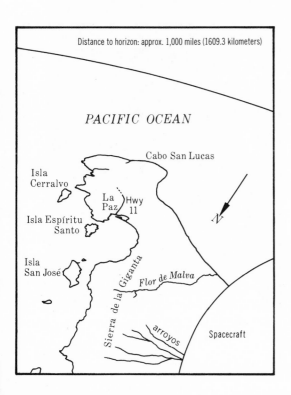

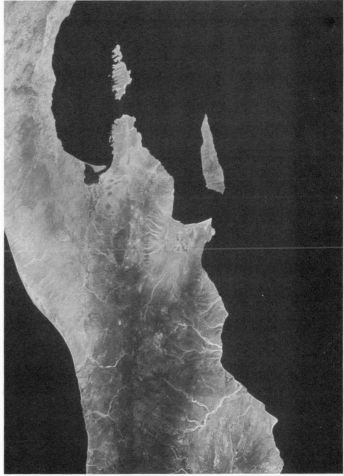

the peninsula has moved 161.5 miles (260 kilometers) to the northwest in the past four million years; in addition, the mouth of the Gulf is separating at the rate of 1.2 inch (3.0 centimeters) per year.

A statistic of this kind is the result of weeks or months of work in the field. The oceanographer has several types of instruments with which to probe the ocean floor, as well as a host of other devices to analyze the water and life in it. To establish the relationship of the sea floor and land of the Gulf of California region, two methods were used: seismic profiles and measurements of the magnetism trapped in the rocks of the ocean bottom.

A seismic profile is a graphic picture of the upper layers of loose sediment and muddy ooze on the ocean floor. To get the profile, a small charge is exploded underwater and the rate of return of bottom echoes is recorded by sensitive microphones in the ship's hull. The magnetic profile is found by towing a magnetometer under the ship. This device measures the magnetism and polarity of sections of the sea floor. Similar instruments are towed beneath aircraft to measure terrestrial magnetism.

The widening and shift of the Gulf of California and of Baja California is some of the most recent support for the continent-drift theory. Promulgated over forty years ago, the theory states that the continents assumed their present relationship by floating over the outer core of the earth. Elsewhere in this atlas are other examples of drift, and the results are shown in the aerial photographs.

More recently, geophysicists have described the earth's crust as being made up of six huge "plates" with some of the continental margins being part of the same plate as the adjacent sea floor.

Mouth of the Colorado River

When Spanish explorers discovered the mouth of the Colorado River and found that California was not an island, they demolished a legend. "California," in a sixteenth-century tale was described as a fertile island off North America peopled by Amazons.

In the accompanying Gemini 4 photograph, the volcanic rocks of the Sierra de las Pintas and the sands of the Gran Desierto show the gap between truth and legend. The nearly straight line along the eastern shore defines an edge of the San Andreas Fault zone. Subtle differences of tone in the water show undersea topography. Unlike most rivers, the Colorado has no delta at present, the river-borne silt being retained behind upstream dams in the United States. The ancient delta is now the soil of the Imperial valley of California.

The Colorado River is the chief source of water for the arid southwestern United States and northwestern Mexico. It is 1,450 miles (2,333.5 kilometers) long from its source in the Rocky Mountains of Colorado. For much of its course it is reddish-brown from the silt it carries. The Spanish name Colorado means red-brown.

NASA

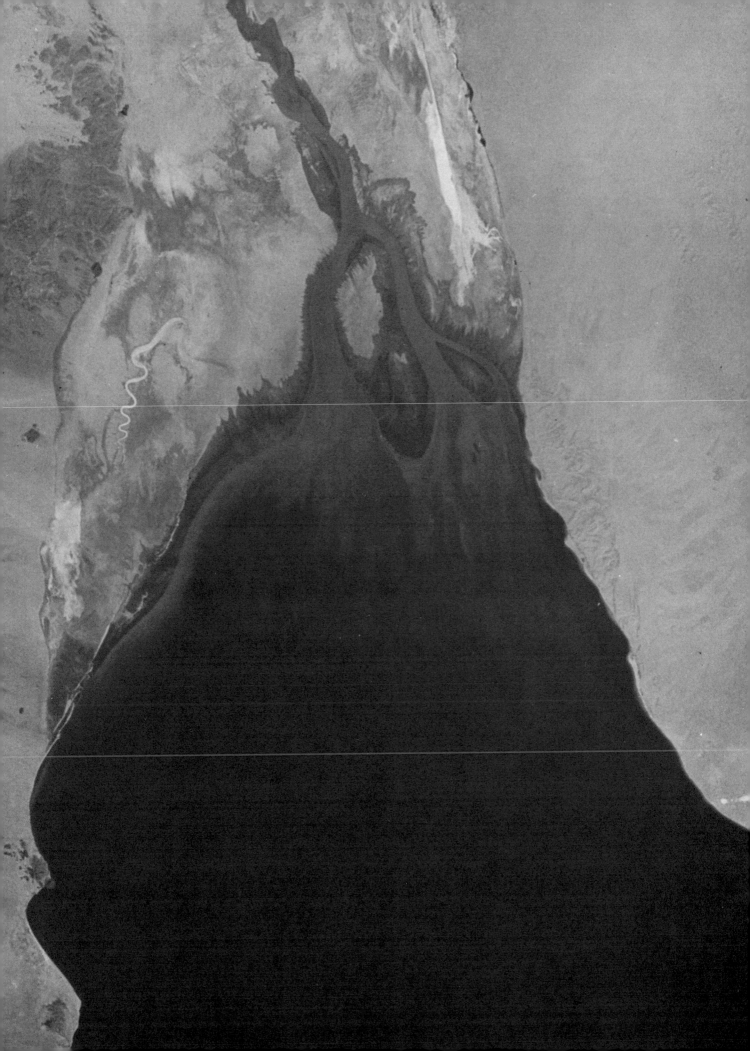

Some of the dramatic geography of Mexico is apparent in this Gemini 12 photograph covering the width of the country. Guadalajara state is a distinctive section of Mexico, especially known for its glassware, pottery, and extensive industrialization.

In the foreground are the ranges of the Sierra Madre Occidental, while those of the Sierra Madre Oriental are marked by the dark line in the distance.   *NASA*

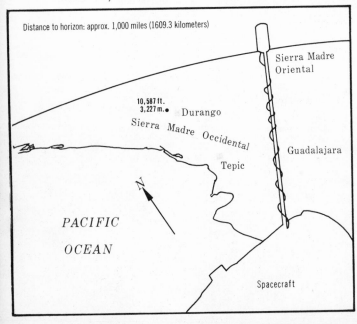

Distance to horizon: approx. 1,000 miles (1609.3 kilometers)

Sierra Madre Oriental

10,587 ft.
3,227 m. ● Durango

Sierra Madre Occidental

Guadalajara

Tepic

N

PACIFIC

OCEAN

Spacecraft

GUADALAJARA

The Sierra Madre Occidental of Mexico's west coast is a southerly extension of the cordilleran system of the United States and Canada. A parallel chain on the east coast is the Sierra Madre Oriental. Between the ranges lies the high rugged Anáhuac Plateau, with Mexico, D.F., at its southern end. The cities, towns, and villages of the plateau are the population center of the country. In the accompanying photograph both Sierras are visible.

The embayment of Nayarit State near the town of Tepic was the original junction between the mainland and the tip of Baja California before the Gulf of California opened as a rift.

In Guadalajara State, the complex geologic formations are a source of gold, iron, lead, mercury, zinc, petroleum, and semiprecious stones, some of which have been extracted since pre-Columbian times.

Chihuahua State is a high desert with a number of peaks over 9,000 feet (2,743.2 meters) high in the mountains ringing the dry basins. Some of the ranches in the region are so large that the workers live in small settlements at great distances from the few towns. There are a few mining sections in the mountains.

NASA

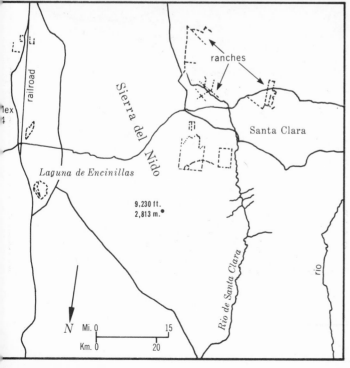

CHIHUAHUA

The Mexican plateau is tipped downward toward its northern end in Chihuahua, but along the eastern slope of the Sierra Madre Occidental it is tipped to the east. This tilt forces the principal river, the Concho, northeast into the Rio Grande. More typical of the state than the Río Concho valley are the "bolsons," or enclosed basins, ringed with folded mountains.

These bolsons are nearly level, often with

playas or dry lakes filling the lowest parts. Some intermittent streams disappear into the sand without even reaching the lower portions of the basin. The bolsons interconnect to form a great desolate plain southeast of Juárez.

Erosion of the mountains is owing almost entirely to water, despite its scarcity on the ground. During the brief rainy season, runoff water accomplishes a great deal because there is little vegetation to absorb the water, no rooted plants to hold the soil cover. Only in the wide valleys with gently sloping bottoms is the water retained. And here much of it is underground, accessible only by drilling.

This lack of available water forestalled extensive agricultural efforts until modern technology brought the rich soil of the alluvium-filled valleys in step with current agricultural practices. Elsewhere in Chihuahua State, mining is the chief enterprise.

The mountain ranges of the state, although rugged, are only a few thousand feet (a few hundred meters) above the general elevation. All the state is above 2,000 feet (609.6 meters), with about half the area being above 5,000 feet (1,524 meters). In most respects Chihuahua very closely resembles the Basin and Range geomorphological province of the United States that covers Nevada and parts of Utah and Arizona. An oblique view of this type of topography is shown in the upper-left portion of the photograph of the Salton Sea in this atlas.

COAHUILA

The rugged sedimentary rock ridges of the Sierra Madre Oriental in Coahuila State are the eastern edge of the mountain systems that circle the Pacific Ocean. Some of the monumental force required to warp and uplift these peaks and ridges was provided by continental drift. This part of Mexico lies near the southern edge of Laurasia — the great protocontinent of the Northern Hemisphere.

In the accompanying Gemini 7 photograph, the triangular shape of the Sierra de la Paila runs at a near right angle to lower ridges, and gives some indication of the complex folding of the region. Numerous mines and quarries dot the hillsides, and a few ranches lie on the valley floors.

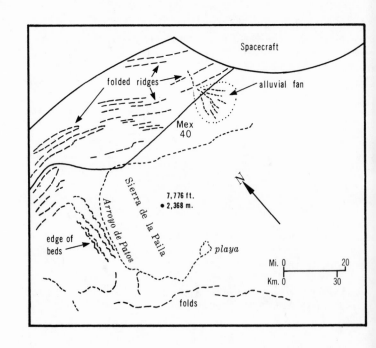

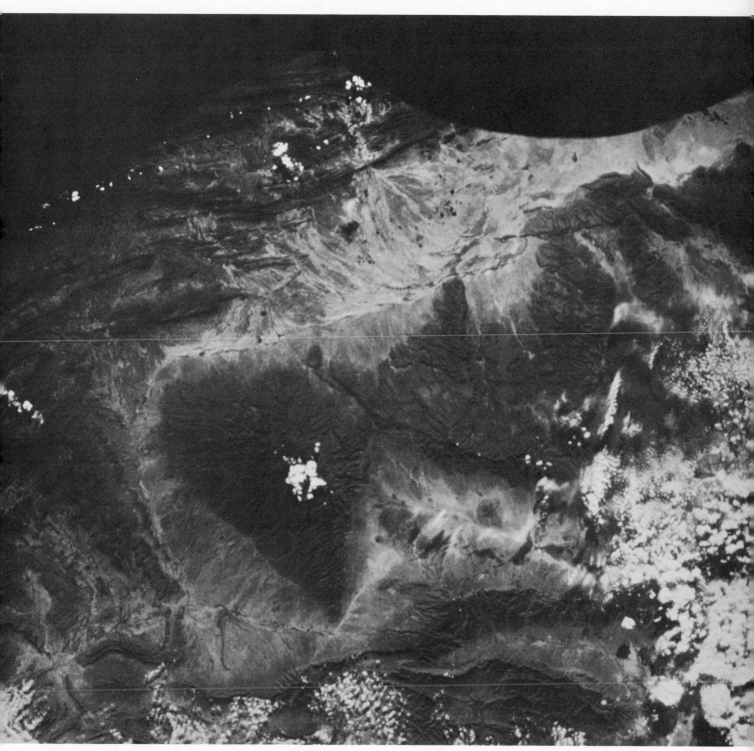

The compressed, folded mountains of Coahuila State are
an important mining and quarrying region of Mexico.
This Gemini 7 photograph shows the eroded folds and
easily traceable drainage patterns. In general these bare
mountains are geologically similar to the forested Appalachians of the United States.

NASA

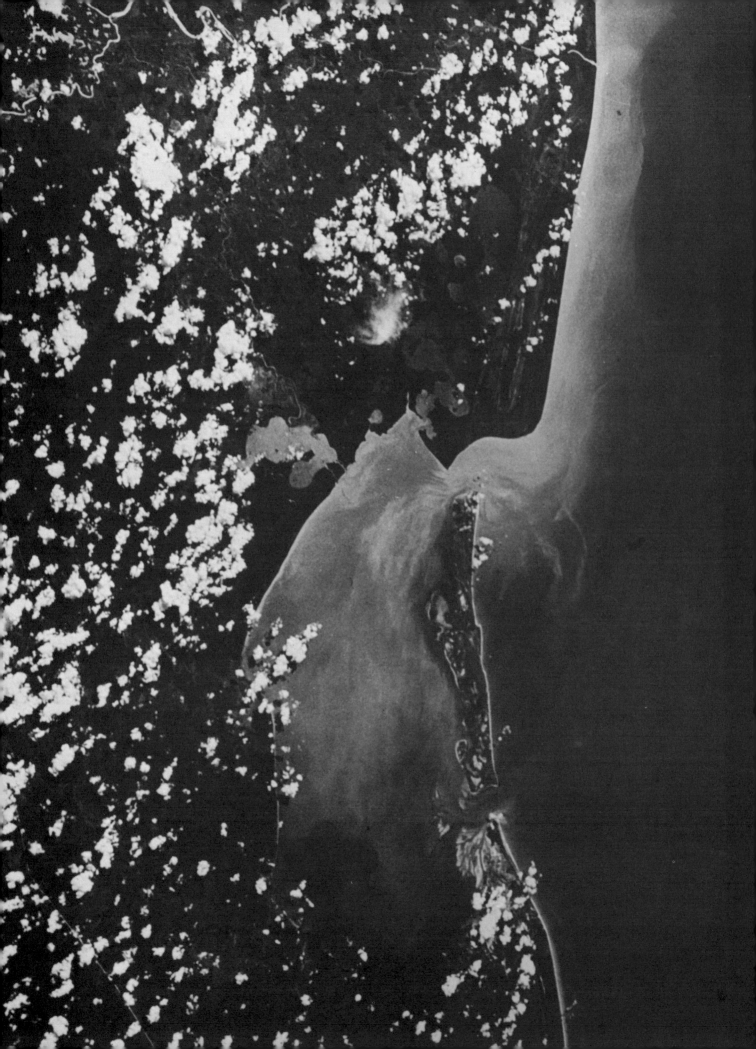

CAMPECHE

Two principal problems in aerial photography of the tropical rain forests of the world are: lack of color contrast in the overall blue-green of the jungle and the generally cloudy skies of the humid climate. The shores of the Bahía de Campeche are representative of the Mexican tropical lowland. This nearly level, humid, often swampy region comprises most of the Yucatan Peninsula of Mexico, inland Guatemala, and British Honduras (Belize).

The largest bay on the Bahía de Campeche is the Laguna de Términos. It is over 40 miles (64.37 kilometers) long and 15 miles (24.1 kilometers) wide. A shallow, swamp-bordered body of water with a barrier island at its mouth, the laguna resembles bays on the Florida peninsula across the Gulf of Mexico. Both the Yucatán and Florida peninsulas are composed of limestone, the calcified remains of tiny sea creatures.

Isla del Carmen, the barrier island, is connected to the mainland at either end by ferry service. The only settlement in the area is the town of Carmen, whose airport, like so many others in the jungle, forms a vital link to the rest of the country. In earlier days this section of the Campeche coast was a pirate haunt. The size of the laguna led early explorers to assume it was part of a strait separating the Yucatán peninsula from the mainland.

The accompanying Gemini 5 photograph shows the value of aerial photography from space for oceanographic work. In the picture, local offshore currents are visible because of their transport of considerable sediment along the shore from the northeast. At the same time, an inshore countercurrent has built up a considerable headland. The old beach line is visible as an extension of the outer shore of Isla del Carmen.

At the eastern entrance to the laguna, the current has kept the channel clear of sediment. A number of small lakes to the west of the laguna are probably delta lakes enclosed by silt borne seaward by the Río Usumacinta. The river rises 250 miles (402.3 kilometers) away in the Sierra de los Chumatanes of Guatemala.

One valuable aspect of space photography in the study of beach and bay erosion is readily apparent in this Gemini 5 photograph of Laguna de Términos. Light-colored sand is borne in suspension by currents, countercurrents, and eddies along the shore, revealing the pattern of water movement.

NASA

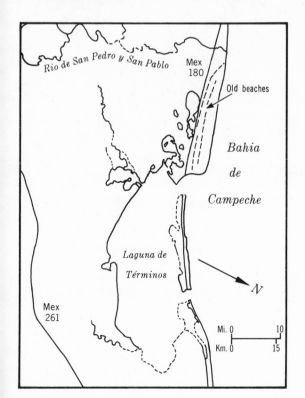

This oblique photograph of Hurricane Gladys provides an even better idea of a tropical cyclone's structure than a vertical view from weather satellites. The central eye is cloud-covered, which is not unusual. As convection currents force the warmest air upward around the eye, other air rushes toward the center in a spiral path, creating very high winds below the storm. In the distance, spicules of towering cumulus clouds indicate an area of especially heavy rainfall. The photograph was taken during the Apollo 7 mission in October 1968.

NASA

Part II
WEST INDIES
CENTRAL AMERICA

The tropical lands surrounding the Caribbean Sea are a unique combination of mild climate and picturesque scenery. At the same latitudes in other parts of the world lie the deserts of North Africa, the mainland masses of India and Southeast Asia, and the northern Philippine Islands.

In the Caribbean (and Atlantic east to Africa), the trade winds that temper the tropical heat also help spawn hurricanes. These great storms begin as revolving eddies of low pressure in the warm air rising from the sun-heated ocean. Many low-pressure areas become small storms called "tropical disturbances," and dissipate. But an average of seven tropical disturbances every year develop into hurricanes. After wreaking great destruction in the Caribbean, some hurricanes cross the Caribbean to strike Central America, Mexico, or the United States.

In geologic structure most of the West Indies are an extension of the great cordilleran system that forms the massive ranges of North America and becomes the Andes in South America. Cuba, Hispaniola, and Puerto Rico are the largest islands, named the Greater Antilles as a group. The Lesser Antilles are the eastern island arc, divided into volcanic mountaintops and low limestone platforms.

The two types of islands meet in Guadeloupe, whose Basse-Terre half is volcanic, with the eastern section, Grande Terre, a low limestone plain. North of the island chains lie the Bahama Islands, whose coral reefs make up the "land" atop a broad submarine platform of limestone.

The Caribbean Sea basin is one of the earth's smaller crustal plates now being intensively studied by geologists as part of the new concept of "plate tectonics" (crustal movements).

The tropical lowlands of the reef-girt shore of British Honduras form the southeastern edge of the Yucatan Peninsula. This view at the border with Mexico shows the reefs as seemingly unbroken, but the roads visible indicate trade routes in an area noted for its hardwood forests.　　　　　　　　　　　　　　　　*NASA*

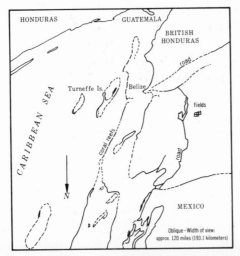

BRITISH HONDURAS (BELIZE)

The east coast of Central America is a low-lying limestone shelf built on the flank of the volcanic chain that fringes the western, or Pacific, shore. Most of the land is swamp and jungle, with coral reefs fringing the shore. Heavy rainfall and the humid climate help produce great forests of mahogany, cedar, rosewood, and lignum vitae, whose woods are staples having many uses. On cleared plantations, chicle, citrus fruits, and rice are grown in economic quantities.

In the accompanying photograph the cloud patterns are typical of the tropics: chains of puffy or low-level cumulus overlain by wisps of cirrus, with some dense patches. Local rainsqualls may result where the cirrus and cumulus merge into large cloud banks.

This Gemini 12 photograph shows the geographic relationship between Florida, the Bahama Islands, and Cuba. It is one of many photographs used in a special study of coastal oceanography, and clearly shows the edge of the Bahama Bank. The study revealed that about 35 percent of the coastal waters of the world's continental shelf can be photographed in detail from spacecraft.

NASA

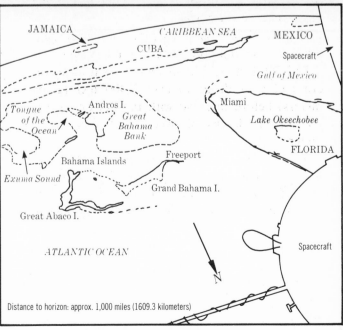

Distance to horizon: approx. 1,000 miles (1609.3 kilometers)

BAHAMA ISLANDS

To North Americans the Bahamas are a kind of nearby cousin to the fabled South Seas. White beaches, palm trees, and coral reefs are common to both places. All coral is the result of warm sea water, and in the Bahamas lies atop a great undersea platform of limestone beds. The islands of the South Seas are of different geologic origin, and are described in a later part of this atlas.

Under self-government since 1964, Bahama

businessmen have changed the once-exclusive winter-resort British colony into a year-round tourist and financial center.

When Christopher Columbus landed in the New World, he first reached the Bahamas. During this and three later voyages he explored many of the islands, was marooned on Jamaica, and established a colony on Hispaniola. Although he was not the first European to visit the Western Hemisphere, his pioneering voyages led to permanent settlements on two continents. In the accompanying Gemini astronaut photograph of the Bahamas, Florida, and Cuba, most of the region laboriously visited by Columbus is visible in a single picture.

The Bahamas are a complex archipelago of low-lying coral. Comer Hill, Cat Island, is the highest point in the islands, with an elevation of 205 feet (62.48 meters). The edges of the limestone Bahama banks break sharply into steep submarine cliffs that drop more than 12,000 feet (3,657.6 meters) on the Atlantic side. On the western edge of the bank is a channel whose deepest segment is 2,877 feet (877 meters). Even more impressive than these cliffs are the deep cul-de-sacs incised into the Great Bahama Bank. The Tongue of the Ocean has a general depth of 4,200 feet (1,280 meters) but deepens rapidly to 6,000 feet (1,829 meters) as it becomes the Northeast Providence Channel. When the channel reaches the Atlantic, its bottom is over 13,000 feet (3,962 meters) below the surface.

Exuma Sound is a smaller, narrower submarine valley than the Tongue of the Ocean. It is over 5,100 feet (1,554.4 meters) deep at its northern end, and drops to over 8,400 feet (2,560 meters) before merging with the bottom of the Atlantic at depths of over 16,200 feet (4,937 meters).

The presence of two such deep dead-end channels is a geologic curiosity, probably caused by erosion by underwater currents. The United States Navy uses the Tongue of the Ocean

(TOTO) for its Atlantic Undersea Test and Evaluation Center (AUTEC) in cooperation with Great Britain and the Royal Navy. Missiles and torpedoes fired into TOTO are tracked from land bases that are stable and offer more precise measurements than could be obtained from ships or buoys.

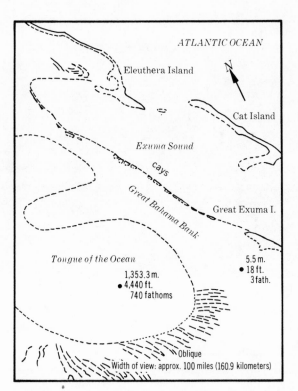

In this view of the Great Bahama Bank, the underwater topography is clearly revealed. The ripple marks are caused by currents cutting into the Bank as they descend into the very deep water of the Tongue of the Ocean. These waters were first sailed by Europeans during Columbus's voyages. The larger cloud formations indicate rainsqualls.

NASA

Acklins and Crooked Islands and Long Cay are coral reefs ringing a limestone submarine platform. The Bight of Acklins is nearly shallow enough to walk across, while the seaward sides of the cays are the edges of undersea cliffs. The sun glint shows a mottled pattern, indicating wind direction.

NASA

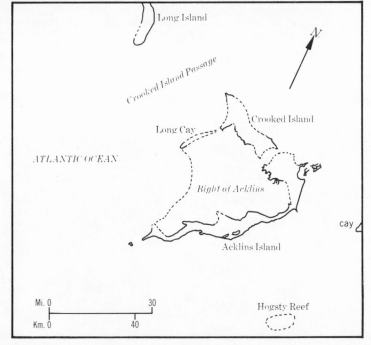

98

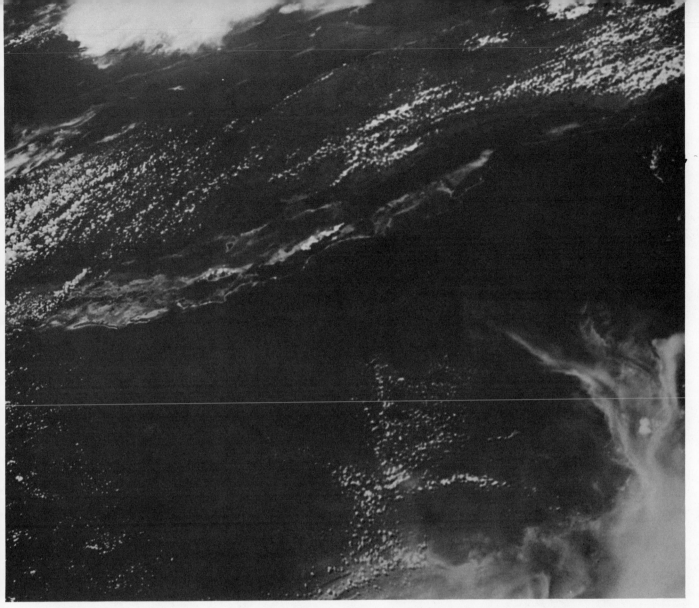

Much of the coastline of north-central Cuba is fringed with islets, reefs, and mangrove swamps, with no useful harbors. Just offshore lies the Old Bahama Channel, a deep natural passage for oceangoing vessels. Most of the island visible in the photograph is in agricultural Camagüey Province.

NASA

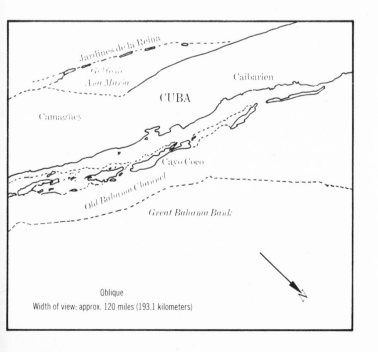

Oblique
Width of view: approx. 120 miles (193.1 kilometers)

Cuba

Cuba, the largest island in the West Indies — nearly as large as the rest of the islands combined — is the only industrial nation in this agriculturally oriented region. The source of Cuba's iron and manganese lies in its hilly regions, part of the folded mountains of the cordilleran system. Most of the island, however, is low-lying and planted in sugarcane, tobacco, sisal, and other crops.

Cuba sits on a limestone pedestal whose sediments surround all but the peaks of the Caribbean arc of mountains. To the north, the Old Bahama Channel defines a deep cut in the sea floor. To the south, the Bartlett Trough forms a trans-Caribbean gash to join the Puerto Rican Trench, the deepest part of the entire Atlantic Ocean.

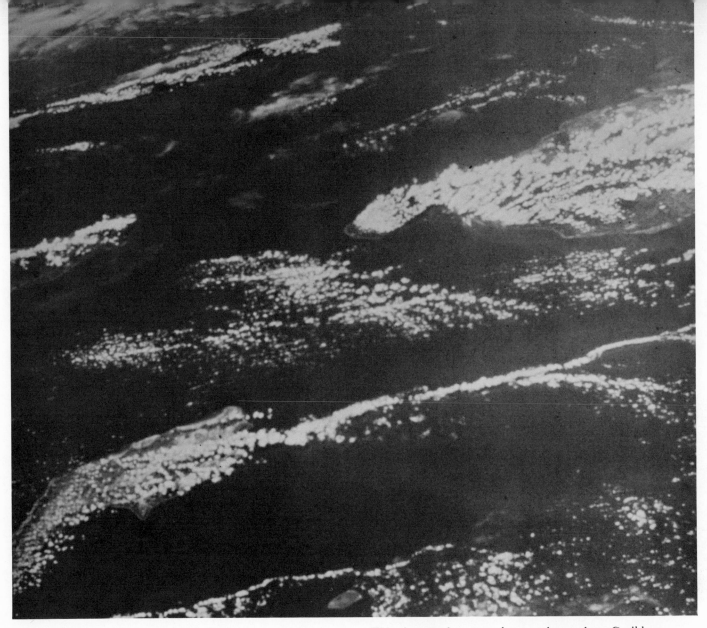

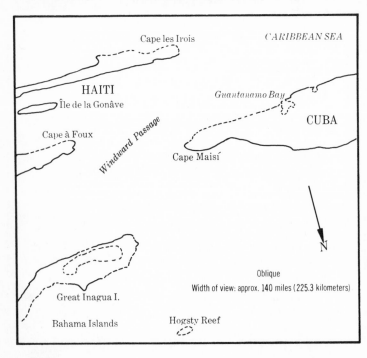

This view southwestward across the northern Caribbean shows the close geographical and geological relationship between the main islands of the region. Although Cuba and Haiti are separated by a deep undersea depression, a geologic trend connects the two. Another segment of the same trend connects Jamaica with the Haitian half of the island of Hispaniola.

NASA

Caribbean Sea

Detailed mapping of the Caribbean Sea floor shows it to be one of the most rugged enclosed ocean basins in the world. It is one of the few pieces left of the gap between the two great continental masses of Laurasia and Gondwanaland.

Geologists today more readily include submarine geology in their world view than in years past. Part of this view is concerned with deter-

At Guadeloupe the volcanic islands of the inner belt making up the Antilles merge with the outer line of limestone islands facing the Atlantic Ocean. In eons past the Caribbean islands formed a straight line before being pinched into a loop when North and South America drifted toward each other. The same effect can be seen in the islands of the Scotia Sea between the tip of South America and the Antarctica Peninsula.

mining how the continents developed. One area of study is island arcs — the semicircular chains such as the Antilles, Japan, and Indonesia. In the Caribbean, from Cuba to the coast of South America, a stepping-stone island chain sits atop a narrow submarine ridge. Inside the Caribbean, Jamaica and a few coral-topped banks mark areas of offshore shallow water. With no nearby continental masses to provide river-borne silt, the banks and shore of the islands are built up of limestone. The shallow water over the banks and along the shore provides an environment for coral.

As a warm-water sea creature, coral thrives throughout the Caribbean, creating a hazard to navigation but gradually enlarging the land areas, and, when broken up by waves, is the regions chief source of sand.

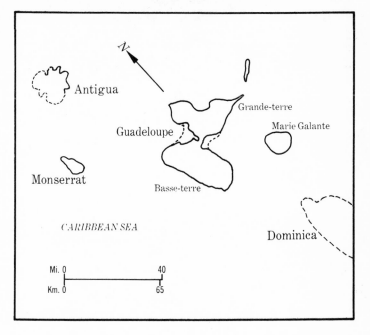

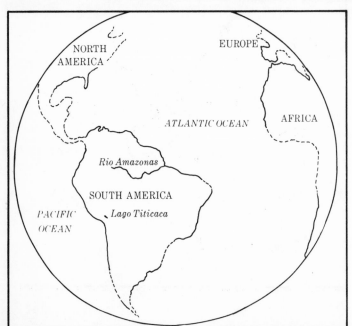

NORTH
AMERICA

EUROPE

ATLANTIC OCEAN

AFRICA

Rio Amazonas

SOUTH AMERICA

Lago Titicaca

PACIFIC
OCEAN

The close-fitting outlines of South America and Africa, visible in this satellite photograph, first suggested the continental-drift theory to geologists. Taken from an altitude of 22,300 miles (35,888.3 kilometers) by ATS 3, the photograph also shows the intricate weather patterns of both Northern and Southern hemispheres.

NASA

Part III

SOUTH AMERICA

This continent is the original America. It was named for the navigator Amerigo Vespucci by Martin Waldseemüller, a sixteenth-century mapmaker. Vespucci explored most of the northern and eastern coast of the continent, and mapped it with considerable accuracy. He also determined that it was not part of Asia.

Any description of South America must be in dramatic terms. The Río Amazonas is one of the longest river systems in the world, and carries a record volume of water to the sea. The world's largest tropical rain forest is in the upper Amazonas Basin, where over 160 inches (406.4 centimeters) of rain falls each year.

In contrast to the wet lowlands of the northeast segment of the continent and the temperate climate of the southeast are the cold dry heights of the Cordillera de los Andes. Here, lakes and playas of considerable size lie in great intermontane basins, second in dimension only to the Tibetan Plateau. Surrounding the basins are even higher mountains, some of which are active volcanoes.

The western slope of the Andes drops precipitously into the Pacific and continues underwater to the bottom of an ocean trench. From the crest of the Andes to the depths of the trench, the land drops over 44,000 feet (13,410 meters) in about 150 air miles (241.4 kilometers).

Once a pirate haunt, the Spanish Main; the north coast of South America today is a tourist attraction and petroleum center. Clouds cover the mountains of Venezuela, an extension of the Andes. Aruba, Curacao, and Bonaire are part of the Netherlands Antilles, and the other islands centers of the local pearl fishing industry.
NASA

Venezuela

In northwest Venezuela, pinched between the mountain ranges Sierra de Perijá and Sierra de Méida, lies a huge basin of sedimentary rock containing some of the world's most extensive petroleum reserves. The lowest part of the broad valley is filled by Lago Maricaibo, part of the reason for the country's nickname: "Little Venice."

The mountain ranges join south of the lake, and are the northern extension of the great Andean chain. For economic reasons most of Venezuelan life is concentrated along the Caribbean shore. Inland lies a relatively unexplored highland region around whose foot flows the Río Orinoco.

Off the coast lie the Dutch islands of Aruba, Curaçao, and Bonaire, where giant refineries process Venezuelan oil for shipment, mostly to the United States.

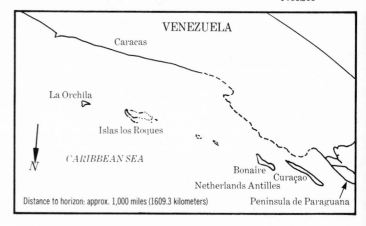

VENEZUELA
Caracas
La Orchila
Islas los Roques
CARIBBEAN SEA
N
Bonaire
Curaçao
Netherlands Antilles
Peninsula de Paraguana
Distance to horizon: approx. 1,000 miles (1609.3 kilometers)

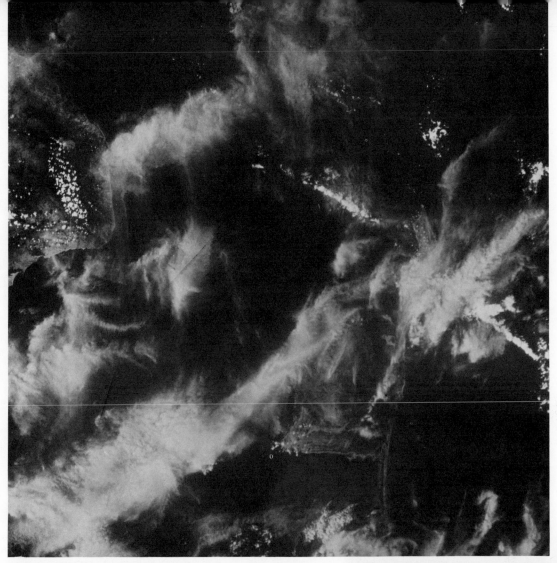

This closeup view of the Golfo de Venezuela and Aruba shows two cloud systems lying across one another because of different wind directions at their elevations. Aruba is a barren rock island, and the Peninsula de Paraguaná is formed from marine deposits, which are also filling in the Golfo de Coro.

NASA

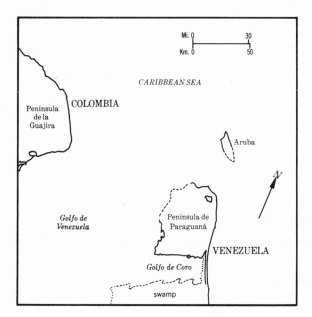

Typical of the highly organized petroleum industry is this refinery on the coast of Venezuela. An intricate network of pipelines from distant wells moves raw petroleum to the refinery for processing. The oil is stored temporarily, then pumped aboard tankers at an offshore pierhead.

Mobil Oil Corporation

105

Good weather in the tropics often means cloudy, but not necessarily rainy, skies. Cumulus clouds form over land, leaving the waterways and ocean well defined. This Gemini 10 photograph shows most of the coast of Guyana and the extensive delta of the Río Orinoco.

NASA

Farther south along the coast of South America, and overlapping the previous photograph, is this view of Surinam. Here, despite the lack of clouds, the even-toned jungle of the coastal plain appears featureless. Offshore, river-borne silt is visible as it is carried along the coast.

NASA

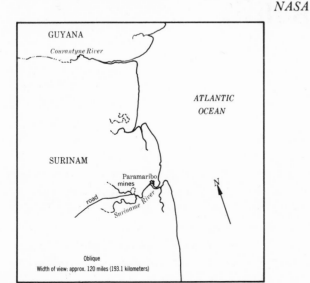

Guyana
SURINAM

In the continental tropics, where the average amount of cloud cover, over the year, is from 40 to 60 percent, aerial photography is difficult. Further, the monotone green of the vegetation conceals natural features. An exception is the coastal regions and waterways where temperature differences between the relatively cool water and warmer land are reflected in the cloud patterns. Rising warm humid air coalesces into clouds over land, leaving the waterways cloud-free paths.

Although land-water patterns can be determined, despite the clouds, in these photographs, new electronic techniques using radar to pierce the cloud cover are being developed to allow accurate detailed aerial photography in the tropics.

In the photographs of portions of Guiana and Surinam, the problems of aerial photography in the tropics are apparent. Guiana is heavily forested from the coastal plain to the interior highlands on the border with Venezuela. Sugar and rice are grown near the coast, and industrial diamonds, bauxite, and gold are mined from the rivers flowing out of the highlands.

Surinam, or Netherlands Guiana, became a Dutch colony in exchange for New York in 1667, after the second of three successive wars with England. No longer a colony, Surinam is now an equal partner with the homeland in national affairs. Like Guiana to the north and French Guiana to the south, the coastal plain is devoted to agriculture. Recently, oil was discovered, which, with hydrolelectric projects, bauxite mining, and the shrimp-fishing industry, is slowly changing the pattern of land use.

In this Gemini 9 photograph the western wall of the Andes is seen in a vertical view. From the snow-capped peaks to the Pacific coast is 60 air miles (96.5 kilometers). The vertical distance from the highest peak to sea level is 22,205 feet (6,918 meters), or a little over 4 miles (6.4 kilometers). The line of peaks represents the continental divide, with water in rivers flowing north-eastward ultimately reaching the Atlantic at the mouth of the Río Amazonas. Many communities in this region were destroyed by the June, 1970, earthquake. *NASA*

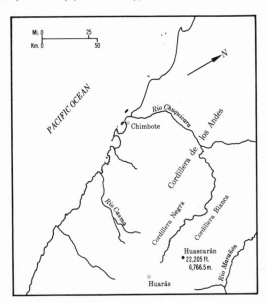

Peru Bolivia Chile

Of the world's great cordillera, only the Himalayas are larger, higher, and more massive than the Andes. The two have great similarities, with high peaks towering over great plateaus, and both are deeply cut by great valleys. Nearly fifty peaks in the Andes reach a height of more than 20,000 feet (6,096 meters), with the highest, Cerro Aconcagua, rising to 22,834 feet (6,959.8 meters).

Each of the Andean republics has important differences, despite their origins as Spanish colonies and their common link, the Andes. Latitude,

the dimensions of the mountains, and the Pacific Ocean vary to create distinctive nations. Most of South America is south of the equator, but the lower elevations have a tropical climate, whereas the high plateaus are barren, dry, and windswept.

In Peru, the great pre-Columbian civilization that culminated in the Incas created a standard of living still unexcelled in the Andes. Cuzco was the last Inca capital, and it represented the ability of man to colonize Andean heights. Quito, Ecuador; Lima, and Machu Picchu, Peru, have archaeological remnants of a civilization that was better adapted to the region than the Spanish conquistadores.

The Pacific coast of Peru is cooled by the Humboldt, or Peru, Current sweeping up from the southern Pacific. The plankton-rich waters abound in fish, and the catch from Peruvian vessels is the largest in the world. Onshore lie

The mining district of central Peru and Lima, the capital, with its port of Callao, are shown in this Gemini 9 photograph. Little or no vegetation conceals the rugged terrain, once spanned by the roads of the Inca Empire.
NASA

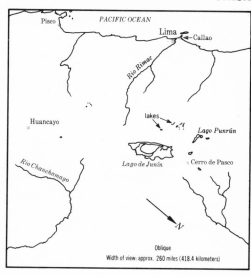

Lago Titicaca is the highest body of water in the world with steamer service. The surface of the lake is 12,506 feet (3,811.0 meters) above sea level. La Paz, the capital of Bolivia, nestles in the barren mountains near the lake. To the south is the great plateau, or Altiplano, of the Andes.

NASA

great deposits of guano, a compound of bird droppings and their food refuse, rich in nitrates and a valuable fertilizer.

Most of the Altiplano, the great central plateau of the Andes, is in Bolivia. This landlocked nation shares Lago Titicaca with Peru. The lake is the highest navigated body of water in the world, with an area of 3,200 square miles (8,288 square kilometers), and a length of 122 miles (196.3 kilometers).

La Paz, the capital and chief city of Bolivia, is near the southeastern end of the lake. Farther south, the Altiplano is barren, with few towns, and limited resources. Much of the Bolivian economy depends on tin mines in the Cordillera Central branch of the Andes. Bolivia east of the Andes covers a part of the continental interior, a fertile region as yet little settled.

Chile lies entirely on the Pacific slope of the Andes. Most of the economy involves the production of copper, iron, gold and less well known but important minerals such as molybdenum and manganese. Along the coast north of Antofagasta is the driest desert in the world, the Atacama. At the city of Iquique not a drop of rain fell in one fourteen-year period, and in an inland valley nearby rain has not been recorded since the beginning of European settlement in the sixteenth century.

Southern Chile is cold and damp in winter, and exposed to winds that blow completely around the world, unhampered by any land. The coast culminates in the island of Cape Horn, separated from Antarctica by Drake Passage. Central Chile, location of the capital, Santiago, and the important port of Valparaiso, is the only part of the entire continent with a Mediterranean climate, reminiscent of the Spanish homeland of the early settlers.

This Apollo 7 view of the coast of Chile, near Antofagasta, includes the Atacama Desert. Some parts of this, the driest desert in the world, have never had a recordable rainfall. Inland, great salt flats lie in the mountain basins of the Andes. The international boundaries of Chile, Bolivia, and Argentina meet near the center of the photograph.

NASA

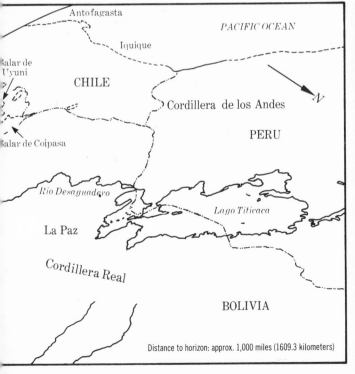

Antofagasta

Iquique

PACIFIC OCEAN

Salar de Uyuni

CHILE

Cordillera de los Andes

N

PERU

Salar de Coipasa

Rio Desaguadero

Lago Titicaca

La Paz

Cordillera Real

BOLIVIA

Distance to horizon: approx. 1,000 miles (1609.3 kilometers)

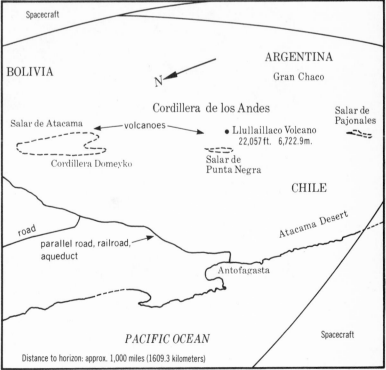

Spacecraft

BOLIVIA

ARGENTINA

Gran Chaco

N

Cordillera de los Andes

Salar de Atacama ← volcanoes → • Llullaillaco Volcano
22,057 ft. 6,722.9m.

Salar de Pajonales

Cordillera Domeyko

Salar de Punta Negra

CHILE

road

parallel road, railroad, aqueduct

Atacama Desert

Antofagasta

PACIFIC OCEAN

Spacecraft

Distance to horizon: approx. 1,000 miles (1609.3 kilometers)

111

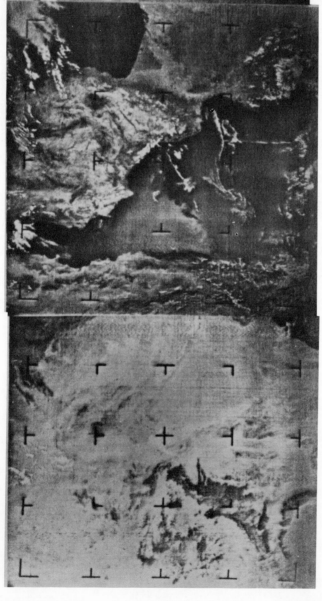

Western Europe and part of North Africa are shown in the three pictures of this Nimbus 1 photomontage. The angular lines are fiducial marks in the satellite's lens system that permit accurate measurements on the photographs after they are received by ground stations.

NASA

Part IV
EUROPE

Although Europe is the second smallest continent (Australia is smaller), its geology and geography are nearly as varied as any of the larger continents. Centuries of habitation, exploration, and scientific investigation have provided not only a detailed picture of European geology and geography but most of the basic concepts of these sciences as well.

Europe was once part of the precontinental land mass Laurasia, which lay north of the Tethys Sea — a much larger version of the present Mediterranean. The essentially east-west linearity of European mountain trends is the principal contrast with the landforms of the Western Hemisphere. The Mediterranean creates a natural separation from Africa, and on land, the Ural Range of the Union of Soviet Socialist Republics is generally used to define the boundary with Asia.

During the Pleistocene Ice Ages Europe was nearly ice free south of latitude 50 at a time when North America was blanketed by the great glacier to a point 10 degrees of latitude (690 miles or 1,100.4 kilometers) farther south. The generally colder climate and high elevation of the Alps, Pyrenees, and a few other mountain ranges caused them to be glacier covered during the Ice Ages.

The folded mountains of Europe, especially the Alps, are formed of great overlapping drapes of sedimentary beds in which the rock flowed as if it were viscous. Scattered throughout the continent are remnants of ancient volcanoes. In Italy the active volcanoes Vesuvius, Stromboli, and Etna are reminders of the forces that shape the land.

Structurally, Europe is divided into four main sections: the Baltic Shield, composed of older rocks stabilized into a broad, low dome with the Baltic Sea in the center; the Caledonian Belt of folded mountains running northeast from Ireland and the English Midlands through Norway which are geologically part of the Appalachians; the Hercynian Ranges, a folded east-west group from Wales to France to Germany; and the Russian Platform, made up of a wedge of flat, thin, sedimentary beds over European U.S.S.R., eastern Europe, and the southern shore of the North Sea.

The bulk of the eighteenth-century Royal Palace dominates this view of Stockholm with a portion of the Old Town, or City of Bridges, at the lower left. Stockholm is built on a number of islands in sheltered waters off the Baltic Sea. Helgeandsholmen, the island on which the Royal Palace and Old Town are situated, was one of three islands fortified when the city was established in 1252.

Swedish Information Service; photo by Oscar Bladh

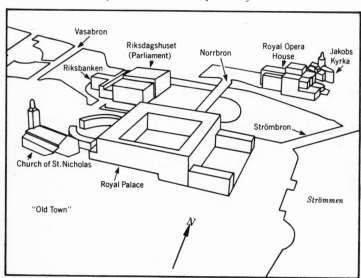

Sweden
Norway

The mountainous boundary between Norway and Sweden delineates an important geological boundary for most of its course. Norway, from Stavanger northwest, is a series of folded mountains deeply cut by glaciers. The numerous islands along the Norwegian coast indicate that the

Wood-processing plants like this one near Karlskoga are a common sight in Sweden. Cut logs are stacked on the fringes of a man-made pond, then floated to the main plant, at lower center in the photograph. Standing timber in the photograph is typical of the one-half of Sweden that is forested.

Swedish Information Service; photo by Oscar Bladh

region was "drowned" by a rise in sea level when the great glaciers of the Ice Ages melted. Where the trough-like valleys once filled with ice have been inundated by the sea they are called fjords.

Along narrow shelves of nearly level land lining some of the fjords, small farms lie at the bottom of the towering cliffs, and the sea is used as a commercial waterway. The link with the sea is strongest on the coast where the great fishing fleets are based.

Just as the geography of Norway turned the

Nordkapp, the northernmost important point in Europe, rises about 1,000 feet (304.8 meters) from the Barents Sea. It lies in nearly the same latitude as Point Barrow, Alaska, the northernmost point in the United States. Most of the cape's erosion is mechanical when winter ice cracks the outer surface.

Widerøe's Flyveselskap

economy into maritime channels, Sweden's forested mountains and abundant hydroelectric resources created a strong industrial base of wood products, with extensive manufactures from local minerals. Part of Sweden's industrial effort is maritime, especially in the shipbuilding field.

Sweden's rocks are part of the Baltic Shield, a region of ancient sediments transformed into granites over aeons of time by chemical and mechanical geologic processes. Most of the rocks in Sweden are over 1,000 million years old.

116

This view of Langfjorden dramatically shows the glacially carved trough valley form of a typical Norwegian fjord. The mountains on the distant skyline are about 30 miles (48.2 kilometers) from the viewpoint. Small farms line the gentler slopes, and the waters of the fjord are used as a trade route.

Widerøe's Flyveselskap

Trondheim, Norway, was founded in 997 as Nidaros. Its cathedral, left center in the photograph, has been described as the finest Gothic cathedral in Scandinavia. The city is the commercial center of an agricultural area and also an important port.

Widerøe's Flyveselskap

Map labels:
- Hyde Park
- Belgrave Sq.
- Kings Road
- Mi. 0 — 1/2 — 1
- Km. 0
- Palace Gardens
- Constitution Hill
- Green Park
- Piccadilly
- Victoria Station
- Buckingham Palace
- Vauxhall Bridge Road
- Birdcage Walk
- St. James's Park
- The Mall
- Victoria St.
- Westminster Abbey
- New Scotland Yard
- Whitehall
- River Thames
- Houses of Parliament
- Vauxhall Bridge
- Lambeth Bridge
- Big Ben Tower
- Westminster Bridge
- flow →
- r.r. bridge
- Lambeth Palace
- Royal Festival Hall
- → N

This photomontage covers the political, clerical, and regal sections of the British capital. Many of the buildings and streets noted in the key map are internationally famous for their historic and literary associations. The irregular street plan indicates the gradual spread of the urban area over many centuries.

Fairey Surveys, Ltd.

GREAT BRITAIN

England

Aerial photography in the United Kingdom has been used in a variety of scientific and technical fields for over fifty years. British interest in cartography, archaeology, town planning, and forestry has centuries of well-kept records and maps as references. Aerial photography has been readily fitted into the pattern as a new research tool.

The photographs in this section show sites spanning British history. In the views of London and Winchester, old street patterns and historic buildings in the cities' core areas show how small, by today's standards, these two great medieval centers were. London was first settled as the Roman garrison town of Londinium. Part of the Roman wall, revealed by the street pattern of today, is noted on the key map.

Winchester has been an important center successively to the ancient Britons, Romans, Saxons, Normans, and English. During Norman times, Winchester and London were joint capitals of the newly conquered country. The city was earlier the capital of the Anglo-Saxon kingdom of Wessex, whose most famous king, Alfred the Great, was nominal ruler of England during the ninth century.

The White Horse of Uffington is the most well known of several such figures in England, made by cutting away the turf to the underlying chalk. Its first-century-B.C. designers never were able to see their design from afar as it appears in the aerial view. Also from air the relationship is apparent between the White Horse, Uffington Castle (an Iron Age hill-fort circa second century B.C.), the Berkshire Ridgeway, part of the ancient track of the Icknield Way; and Dragon's Hill, where St. George fought the Dragon (or White Horse) according to local tradition.

In the aerial view showing part of Hadrian's Wall, some idea of Roman defense policy is apparent. The wall was aligned to cross the river

119

"The City," London's financial and trade center was founded as a Roman fort before A.D. 61. In this aerial view the old Roman Wall can be traced and also the area burnt out in the Great Fire, 1666. Today, modern skyscrapers vie with St. Paul's cathedral for domination of the skyline. Many of the new buildings are on sites bombed out during World War II.

Fairey Surveys Ltd.

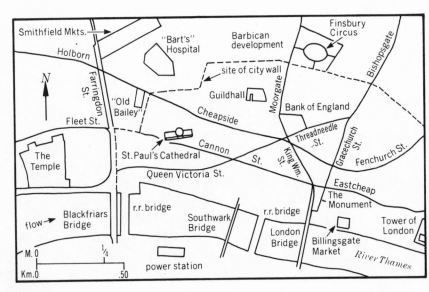

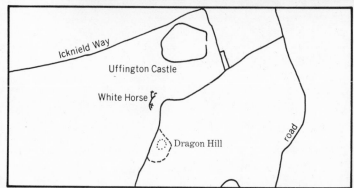

The irregular outline of Uffington Castle is typical of many Iron Age forts found in England. Nearby, the White Horse is an ancient tribal emblem, 360 feet (109.7 meters) long, cut into the chalk of the hillside. Just above the fort runs the Icknield Way, part of a neolithic system of hilltop tracks that are still public rights-of-way.

Fairey Surveys, Ltd.

Hadrian's Wall and the Roman fort of Cilurnum, on the River North Tyne in Northumberland, are visible despite modern field lines. The fort is on a private estate, Chesters, but is supervised by the national government. Details of Roman forts are so well known that the names of military units who served in them have been recorded.

Fairey Surveys, Ltd.

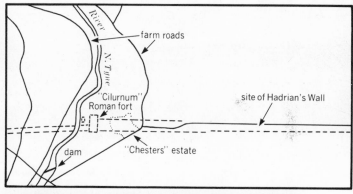

Early settlement of Winchester, Hampshire, is evident in the Iron Age fort on St. Catherine's Hill. The first earthworks of the fort were thrown up in the third century B.C. Winchester Cathedral dominates the city itself, once the co-capital with London.

Fairey Surveys, Ltd.

Tyne at a chosen spot, and the fort of Cilurnum (now called Chesters) was sited to defend the gap in the wall and also have the river as a source of water.

The use of aerial photography in archaeology is not limited to still-standing or excavated sites. In Appendix II an example of aerial photography as a means of discovery, of an English site, is described.

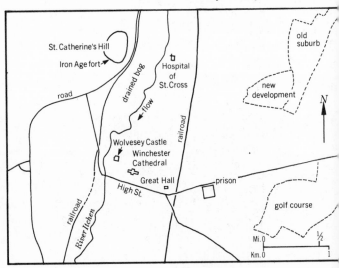

122

Scotland

Edinburgh

The Scottish capital is an example, like New York City, of the influence of geology on urban sites. Both city cores were initially determined by geologic features: New York by relatively narrow Manhattan Island, and Edinburgh by the defensive prominence of Castle Rock. In more recent times, the bedrock of Manhattan led to the development of very tall buildings, while Edinburgh's eighteenth-century street plans are some of the most elegant anywhere, and the dry lochs became natural nineteenth-century transportation corridors.

Castle Rock and Arthur's Seat (no connection with the English King Arthur) are both remnant plugs of hardened lava — the cores of extinct volcanoes whose cones have eroded away.

Many aspects of Scottish history and culture are connected with the events and people of the national capital, Edinburgh. Arthur's Seat, Castle Rock, Salisbury Crags, and Calton Hill are remnants of volcanoes, which project through layers of coal, limestone, and sandstone.
Fairey Surveys, Ltd.

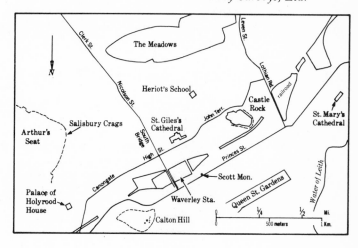

123

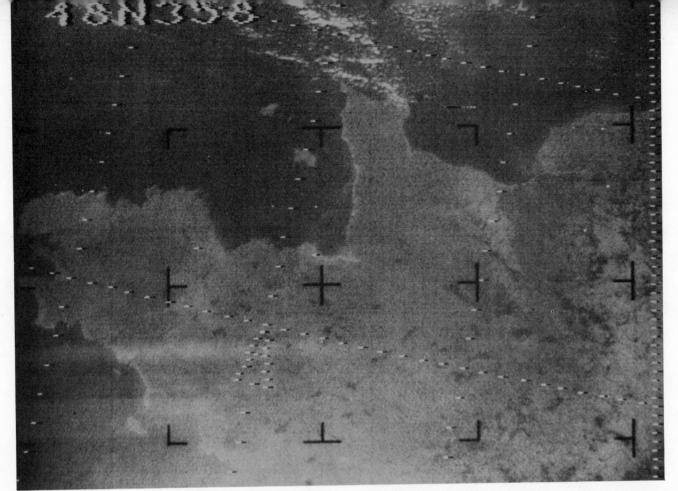

Most of Brittany and Normandy — the historical Armorica — are shown in this Nimbus 1 photograph. The intricate shoreline of the Breton peninsula is indicative of a coastline of submergence. An overall rise in worldwide sea level, interrupted by the last continental glaciation, carried the ocean far inland in this part of France.

NASA

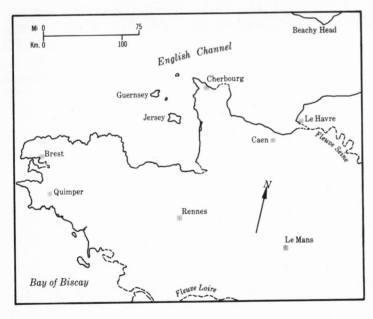

France

About 270 million years ago, Brittany and Normandy straddled what was then the equator. The climate was warm, and great forests of fernlike trees grew and died, eventually to form the coal beds found in the region. At that time the English Channel (called La Manche in France) was a river valley whose waters flowed westward into the geologically youthful Atlantic Ocean. During this epoch the then narrow Atlantic was about 50 million years old. As part of its later development, the Bay of Biscay, southeast of Brittany, opened up about 40 million years ago as northern Spain swung away from the western coast of France.

The present coastline is one of submergence caused by the 400 feet (121.9 meters) worldwide rise in sea level over the past 20,000 years. The Atlantic and Channel waters flow over the broad continental shelf off France and the British Isles to inundate what were once far-inland valleys and plains.

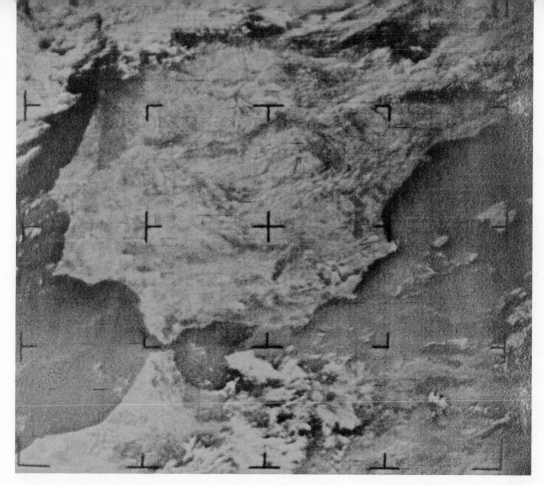

Spain, Portugal, and the coast of Morocco are nearly covered by clouds in this Nimbus 1 photograph. The Straits of Gibraltar, seen in detail in this atlas in Part V, is at the center of a mountain arc bent into a bow by continental drift.

NASA

Spain
Portugal

Geological investigations on land and at ocean depths show that the Iberian peninsula rotated south from France to create the Bay of Biscay. The pivotal point was near San Sebastian, where the Pyrenees meet the Atlantic Ocean. As a part of this rotation, of about thirty degrees, the Pyrenees were uplifted and folded. Such an "opening" of a land mass is called a "sphenochasm" by geologists.

Continental drift is a continuing process, and tensions in the earth's crust from such great movements are sometimes unleashed to create large-scale earthquakes. One such struck Lisbon (Lisboa), Portugal, on November 1, 1755, in a triple shock usually described as the most violent earthquake of recorded times.

The medieval section of Bern, the Swiss capital, nestles in an entrenched meander of the Aar River. Some indication of the depth to which the river has cut into the rock is shown by the height of the Kirchfeld Bridge at the left in the photograph.

Aerofilms, Ltd.

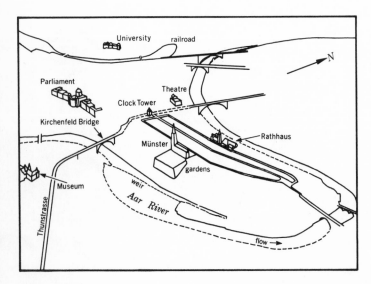

Switzerland

Although the Alps dominate the geography of Switzerland, their height, steep slopes, and narrow valleys limit their availability for settlement or agriculture. Seventy percent of the country's population lives on the intermontane basin of the Central Plateau. The plateau lies between the Alps and the Jura range on the border with France. Glaciation and rivers have cut deep into the region and large lakes fill several of the lower depressions.

Bern (Berne), the national capital, lies near the center of the plateau, on the Aar River. Founded in 1191, the oldest section of the city is an example of medieval town planning at a strategic

Geneva straddles the Rhône River outlet of Lac Léman (Lake of Geneva). In this aerial view some indication is shown of the city's characteristic architecture and favorable position as a gateway to the Central Plateau of Switzerland.

Aerofilms, Ltd.

military location. The medieval community grew on what geologists call a spur of an entrenched meander of the Aar.

In contrast to Bern, Geneva (Genève) developed on the level shores of Lac Léman (or Lake of Geneva) where it empties into the Rhône River. The advantages of this site are as a trade route on the lake, river and roads circling the lake. Geneva and Bern are industrial centers specializing in the precision manufactures for which Switzerland is famous. In architecture, Geneva is nearly unique for its many imposing buildings that house the headquarters of a number of nonpolitical international organizations.

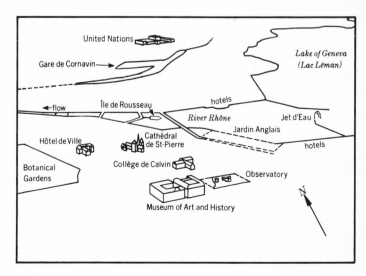

This Nimbus 1 view of southern Italy, Sicily, the Adriatic Sea, and coast of Yugoslavia, Albania, and Greece spans a prong of land believed to have once been part of Africa. The satellite's chief purpose is meteorological observations, which here show considerable cloud cover over the higher elevations of the Balkans.

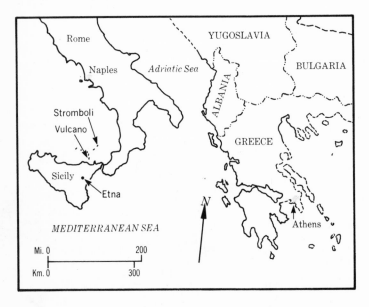

Italy

In Italy and the Adriatic Sea, the concepts of crustal mobility are even more apparent than in the movements of whole continents. Geologic evidence suggests that the Italian peninsula was once part of Africa. As that continent drifted eastward, the peninsula was bent ninety degrees and moved northward across the gap of the ancient Tethys Sea, which separated the northern and southern land masses of Laurasia and Gondwanaland.

The tensions produced by this movement are apparent in the active volcanic chain of western Italy. Volcanoes are generally physically associated with young mountains and the edges of crustal blocks. Vesuvius, Stromboli, and Vulcan — three famous Italian volcanoes — have given their names to volcanic types in geologists' system of classification.

The historic Acropolis and Parthenon stand above the streets of Athens as they have for over 2,300 years. In the near distance is Mount Lycabettos. The rocks of this region are mainly marine deposits, and the resistant crags are of limestone that has metamorphosed to form marble. The architecturally important structures of Athens were built by using locally quarried rock.

NASA

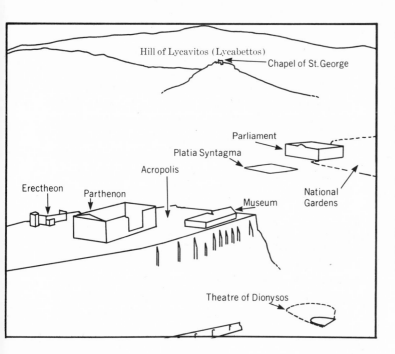

Greece

Aerial photographs such as the accompanying views of Greece have a particular value in the study of history. Cities, trade routes, and the developing patterns of civilization are visible in their natural context.

Athens (Athinai), modern capital of Greece and one of the great historic cities of the Western world, is an urban center surrounding the ancient Acropolis. Settled in neolithic times, the Acropolis reached a peak of development during the sixth and fifth centuries B.C. The Parthenon and Erechtheon are the most prominent structures

129

In this view looking north into the Aegean Sea and mainland Greece, the many islands of the Aegean archipelago are in marked contrast to the open waters of the Mediterranean Sea to the south. Crete, Karpathos, and Rhodes form an arc across the Aegean that also outlines an undersea precipice.

NASA

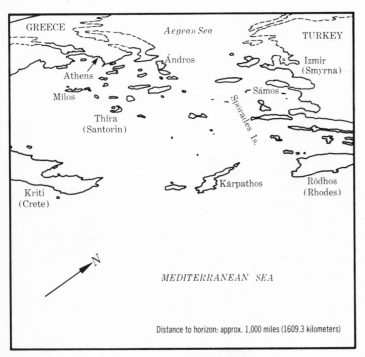

Distance to horizon: approx. 1,000 miles (1609.3 kilometers)

from this period visible in the accompanying photograph.

The scattered islands of the Aegean Sea are peaks remaining after the partial collapse of a mountain chain about 12 million years ago. Before the structure fragmented, it connected Greece, Crete, and Asia Minor (modern Turkey).

Thera (or Santorin), the semicircular island north of Crete visible in the astronaut's view of the Aegean, is a "caldera," or remnant wall of a collapsed volcanic structure. A recent theory suggests that Thera was the site of legendary Atlantis, which vanished in 1400 B.C. when the center of the island erupted in a titanic volcanic explosion. Some evidence, especially the abandonment of the Minoan cities on Crete at the same time, supports many elements of the Atlantis myth.

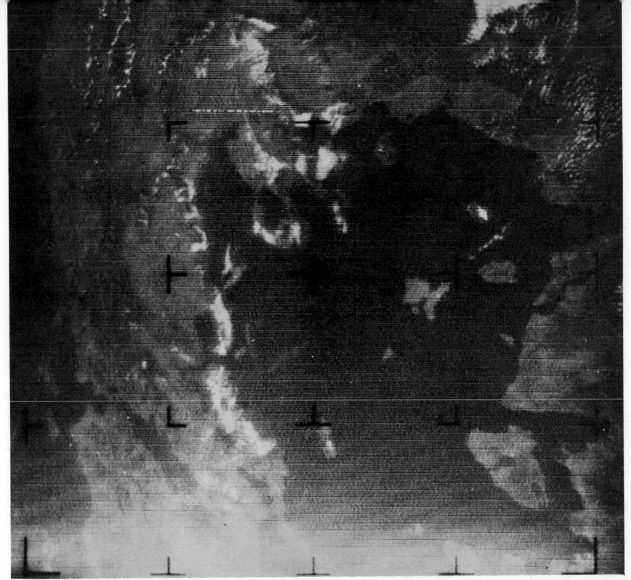

This vertical view of the northern Aegean Sea can be compared with previous photographs to give nearly complete coverage of Greece. The Aegean is a shallow body of water, and in time may disappear if structural changes raise the sea floor. Turkey, at right, forms Asia Minor, a westward extension of the continental mass of Asia.

NASA

The relationship between Africa and Asia is evident in
this Lunar Orbiter 5 photograph made from the vicinity
of the moon. For thousands of years the monsoon and
trade winds of the Indian Ocean have carried commerce
and culture along the coasts of the two largest continents.
NASA

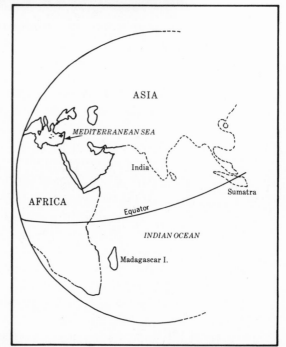

Part V

AFRICA
THE MIDDLE EAST

In development, Africa is the "newest" continent. Geologically, the rocks on its surface are some of the world's oldest. Second only to Asia in size, Africa has few marks of comparison with other continents. It is unique in its relatively smooth coastline, which offers few natural, protected harbors. North Africa is mostly desert, with an Arab population associated with the Middle East. Central Africa is bisected by the equator, and its predominantly hot, humid tropical lands are peopled by a variety of Sudanese, Bantu, and Nilotic black cultures.

South Africa, the chief region of white settlement, differs from tropical Africa in its more temperate climate and phenomenal mineral resources.

The Middle East, an obviously European designation, sometimes refers to the area between the Mediterranean Sea and the Persian Gulf, and is also used to include Iran and the United Arab Republic. Asia Minor, a similar term, includes Turkey with the Middle Eastern countries. In this atlas, Iraq, Iran, and Saudi Arabia are described as part of Asia.

Historically, North Africa is part of the history of successive dominant cultures of the Mediterranean Sea. Central and South Africa have histories only recently noted by Europeans and Americans. During the second half of the nineteenth century, Africa was explored by Europeans, and late in the century eighty years of colonial domination began. Today most of the former colonies are again independent but with national boundaries often superimposed on ancient tribal territories. Man, as an animal, probably first appeared on earth in Africa, and it is perhaps significant that an important part of his effort to survive is again shifting the interest of the world to Africa.

An important part of the geology of Africa are the tremendous gorges of the rift valleys — links in the global system of continental drift. Africa formed a triangular segment of the protocontinent Gondwanaland. Its broad features today are great basins and swells or rises, often of ancient rocks of the basement complex. In various places volcanoes and lava beds project through old formations in situations unique in that they are in the continental interior.

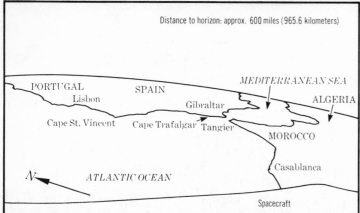

Distance to horizon: approx. 600 miles (965.6 kilometers)

PORTUGAL   SPAIN   *MEDITERRANEAN SEA*
Lisbon   ALGERIA
                    Gibraltar
Cape St. Vincent   Cape Trafalgar Tangier
                              MOROCCO
N   *ATLANTIC OCEAN*   Casablanca
                                        Spacecraft

Once a limit to the known ocean, the Straits of Gibraltar became a gateway to Africa and the New World after the fifteenth-century. The ancients called the heights of Gibraltar (Jebel al-Tarik) to the north, and Jebel Musa, to the south, the Pillars of Hercules. Both are geologically connected in the crust of the earth as part of a westward-facing arc.

NASA

Crossing the undefined southern frontier between Morocco and Algeria and extending into Spanish Sahara are the ridges of a great syncline enclosing the Hamada de Tindouf. Water erosion, even in this arid climate, has cut across the ridges. One of the views of Saudi Arabia in this atlas shows another example of the overall importance of water as an erosional force, even in the desert.

NASA

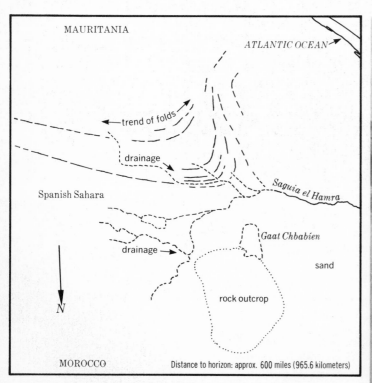

MAURITANIA
                    ATLANTIC OCEAN
            ←trend of folds
        drainage
                        Saguia el Hamra
Spanish Sahara
        drainage
                    Gaat Chbabien
                              sand
            rock outcrop
N
MOROCCO   Distance to horizon: approx. 600 miles (965.6 kilometers)

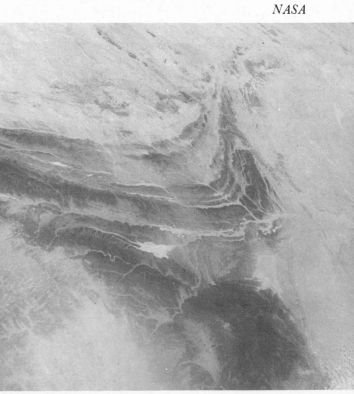

Morocco

SPANISH SAHARA

Morocco is dominated by the three principal ranges of the Atlas Mountains, whose highest peak is Jebel Toubkal (13,664 feet, or 4,165 meters). The northernmost range is the Er Rif. To the south, at a diagonal, lie the Middle Atlas, which form a link with the High Atlas, a folded range of marine sediments. Further south are the Anti-Atlas, which have no geologic connection. Between the Atlas group and Anti-Atlas lies the Oued Sous, a trough of downwarped sediments. The break between the two ranges if further distinguished by a 700-mile (1,126.5-kilometer) fault. Activity along this fault nearly destroyed the Moroccan port city of Agadir a decade ago.

Spanish Sahara defines most of the western edge of the great African desert. The accompanying astronaut photograph and other views of the Sahara in this atlas give some geography of most of northern Africa.

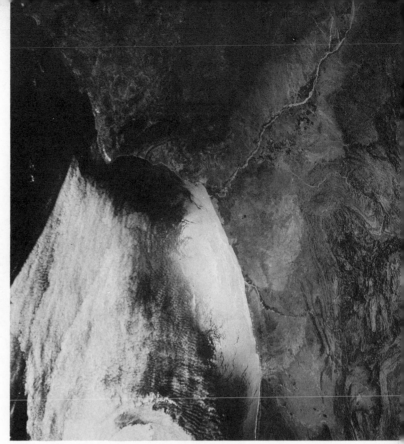

The High Atlas mountains, in the upper portion of this photomontage, are 200 million years younger than the Anti-Atlas to the south. Between the ranges the Oued Sous follows the trend of a fault zone. Movement along this fault devastated the coastal city of Agadir in 1961.

NASA

A closeup aerial view of the "Rock" shows evidence of its limestone composition, once deep under the sea. A British fortification since 1704, Gibraltar is honeycombed with tunnels of the defense system. In recent years neighboring Spain has attempted to negotiate return of this segment of her territory.

Aerofilms, Ltd.

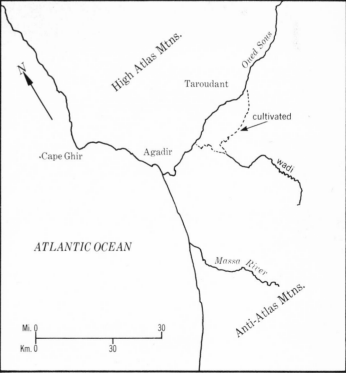

Desert, forest, and sea contrast sharply in this Gemini 5 photograph of Algeria and the Mediterranean. In the lower center dry lakes, or *sebkha,* are light in tone, while strips of darker forest line the mountaintops.

NASA

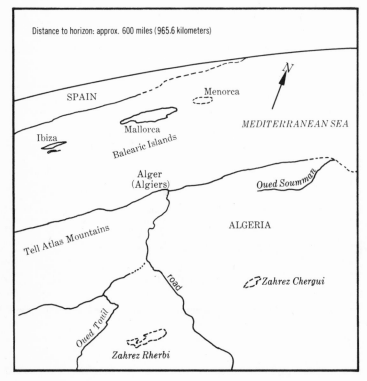

Distance to horizon: approx. 600 miles (965.6 kilometers)

SPAIN

Menorca

N

MEDITERRANEAN SEA

Mallorca

Ibiza

Balearic Islands

Alger (Algiers)

Oued Soumman

ALGERIA

Tell Atlas Mountains

road

Zahrez Chergui

Oued Touil

Zahrez Rherbi

Algeria

Independent since the end, in 1962, of a fierce struggle for self-determination, Algeria is a desert and also a coastal country. Pipelines from the Sahara carry petroleum to Bougie (Bejaia) and Arzew near Oran. These oil fields are vital to a country whose population and economic resources are crowded north of the Atlas Mountains and into the valleys of the Tell or Maritime Atlas. With Morocco and Tunisia, Algeria is known to Arabs as the Maghreb.

Most of Algeria is a part of the Sahara (which means "desert" in Arabic). Geographically, the Sahara is the world's largest and driest desert. It covers an area of Africa of about 4 million square

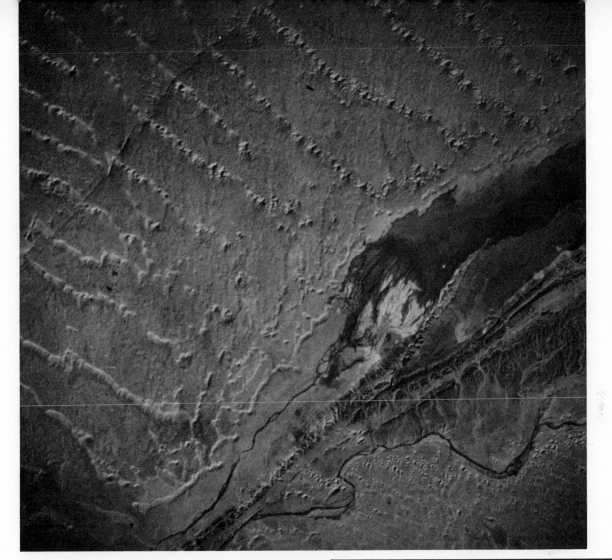

The complex patterns of lines of sand dunes in this photograph show the importance and force of the wind in the desert. Lines of eroded ridges buried by the sand cross the picture. The lake and "river" are transitory features caused by runoff from the distant Atlas Mountains.

NASA

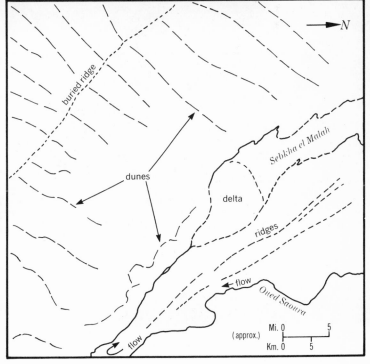

miles (10.4 million square kilometers). Although there are huge sections of dunes (*erg,* in Arabic) or gravel beds *(reg* or *serir,* in Arabic) much of the desert is bare rock of varied relief. Mount Tahat, in southern Algeria, is over 9,000 feet (2,743 meters) high.

Over 10,000 years ago, the Sahara had a wetter climate, when ice covered parts of the Northern Hemisphere. The ubiquitous camel was introduced by the Berbers and adopted by the Arabs, who introduced the oases-caravan mode of life during medieval times.

In parts of the Sahara, saline dry lakes (*sebkha,* in Arabic) provide salt for the nomadic population. The *sebkha* are similar to the playas of North American deserts, and lie in basins of enclosed drainage.

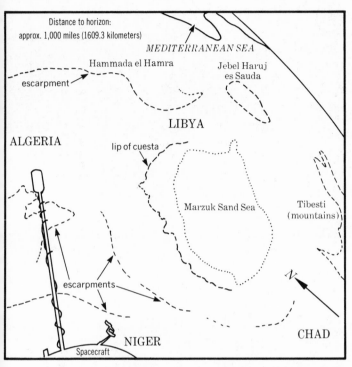

Map labels:
Distance to horizon:
approx. 1,000 miles (1609.3 kilometers)

MEDITERRANEAN SEA

Hammada el Hamra

Jebel Haruj
es Sauda

escarpment

LIBYA

ALGERIA

lip of cuesta

Marzuk Sand Sea

Tibesti
(mountains)

N

escarpments

NIGER

CHAD

Spacecraft

Almost all of Libya is covered in this photograph that clearly shows the desolation of the Sahara. The semicircular feature in the center is a cuesta, an escarpment with a gentle back slope. In the basin formed by the sedimentary rocks of the cuesta lies a huge dune field, the Marzuk Sand Sea.

NASA

Libya

Some idea of the vastness of the Sahara can be had from the accompanying Gemini 11 view covering most of the northeastern part of the great desert. The area in the photograph shows most of Libya and parts of Algeria, Niger, Chad, and, in the distance, the United Arab Republic. Only about one-sixth of the desert is shown in the photograph.

Many of the desert features are on a dramatic scale. The light-colored oval near the center of the photograph is the Marzuk Sand Sea, 250 miles (402.3 kilometers) wide. It is contained by the gently rising rocks of a cuesta whose sedimentary beds were laid down between 225 and 70 million years ago. The term "cuesta" is used by geologists for a feature with a long rise ending abruptly in an escarpment. Like many desert features, it is a Spanish word (meaning hill slope) and was first used in geologic descriptions of the American Southwest.

Northeast of the Marzuk Sand Sea is a volcanic field called Jebel Harnj es Sanda that covers an area of 2,000 square miles (5,180 square kilometers). Another volcanic region in the photograph is the Tibesti, in Chad, shown at the edge of the picture.

Geologic interest in the northern Sahara led to the discovery of petroleum resources, particularly after World War II. By 1957, oil became the chief economic factor in Libya. Modern technology not only requires more petroleum products but also provides the means for more efficient exploration. In an accompanying photograph a typical oil-discovery site is shown. One of the principal features of today's drilling practices is evident in the portability of the equipment, from the derrick to workers' housing.

To many people the Sahara is associated with romantic tales of Berber and Tuareg tribes. The two peoples are the aboriginal inhabitants of North Africa. "Berber" stems from the Latin word *barbari,* which was later used to define the

139

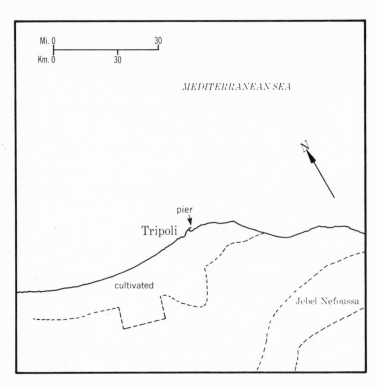

Barbary Coast, nineteenth-century Arab pirate strongholds of the southern Mediterranean shore. But the Berbers have a culture distinctive from that of later invaders, including the Moslem. The Berbers are an agricultural people living in small villages throughout the Sahara. The Tuareg tribes are nomadic, and their caravan trails crisscross the most desolate parts of the Sahara, shown in these photographs.

The Berbers were known to the Egyptians at least as long ago as 2400 B.C. And in the Tibesti, tombs and rock paintings indicate neolithic cultural sites.

This view of an exploration oil-well rig operated by Mobil Oil Libya is a scene repeated many times over in Libya today. Major discoveries since the late 1950's have given the country a sorely needed economic base. When a well comes in (or proves dry), the rig is transported, with its crew, to another site.

Mobil Oil Corporation

Traditionally, maps show water areas in light tones and land contrastingly darker, the reverse of actuality as this photograph shows. Cultivation along the Mediterranean shore near Tripoli is apparent, including a huge palm orchard. The scalloped coastline, with differing sizes of arcs, is characteristic of shallow-water coasts.

NASA

141

This view of the Nile delta and Sinai peninsula is one of the most dramatic photographs taken by the Gemini astronauts. Nearly all the people in the United Arab Republic live on the delta. As it empties into the Mediterranean, the Nile is obviously extending the land area at the Rosetta and Damietta mouths of the river.

NASA

United Arab Republic

In the history of Western civilization, Egypt — the present United Arab Republic — has a special place. Its fascinating temples and pyramids stood as mute remnants of an ancient society until the early nineteenth century, when discovery of The Rosetta Stone clarified the hieroglyphics. Important events in the Old Testament took place in the land of the Pharaohs. In the Gospel according to St. Matthew, the Holy Family fled to Egypt when Jesus was an infant. Alexander the Great founded Alexandria and is buried there in an unknown spot. Julius Caesar, Marc Antony, and Cleopatra lived part of their dramatic lives in Egypt. Through the centuries the mass of the population, the fellaheen (from which stems our word "fellow"), tilled fields watered and flooded by the Nile River.

Today the United Arab Republic, separated by more than a thousand years from ancient Egypt,

is gradually modernizing the country. Much of the U.A.R.'s attempt is based on the country's chief natural resource — the Nile. A series of barrages and dams in the upper stretches of the U.A.R. part of the river are used for better utilization of the water. These man-made devices, and the Suez Canal, indicate the sheer physical effort needed to cope with the inhospitable desert of most of the country.

In aerial photographs taken by the Gemini astronauts, the principal geographic features of the U.A.R. are of a scale easily encompassed in a single picture. The Sinai Peninsula, Red Sea, Suez Canal, and Nile Delta show dramatically in the Gemini photographs. The pictures emphasize the statistic that 99 percent of the people live in only 3-1/2 percent of the country.

This concentration is owing to previous economic dependence on cotton and textiles. In recent years the Sinai Peninsula and shores of the Red Sea have yielded mineral products such as petroleum, coal, phosphates, and manganese in small quantities.

The Suez Canal, which originally opened in 1869, became nationalized by the U.A.R. in 1956 but was closed later that year, reopened and closed again in 1967 after wars with Israel. After the 1956 closing, international maritime interests began construction of gigantic oil tankers and of container ships that obviate use of the canal. The great oil ships circle Africa to reach Europe. Container ships' goods reach Europe or Asia by transshipment across Canada or the United States. In both cases the cost is only a little more than that of the canal route.

Although the Suez Canal was the first waterway capable of handling large vessels between the Mediterranean and the Red Sea, it was not the first such canal. In 1980 B.C. the Pharaoh Sesostris built a canal from the Nile to Lake Timsah, the then northern end of the Gulf of Suez. Later, this canal silted up, was partly reopened by the Pharaoh Necho about 600 B.C.,

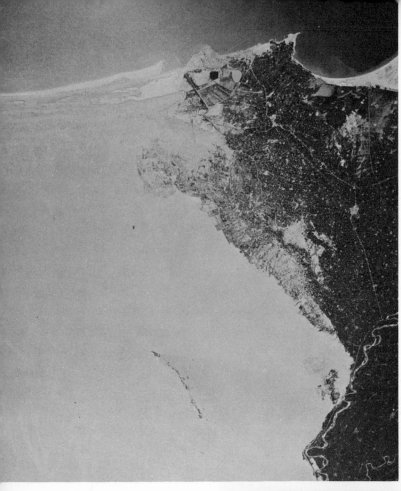

Extension of land under cultivation is apparent in this Gemini photograph of Alexandria and the western delta. The Wadi el-Natrun, a chain of below-sea-level salt lakes, lies in one of several depressions in the U.A.R. west of the Nile. Some reclamation schemes envision flooding such depressions so that river silt creates tillable soil.

NASA

Extensive use of the waters of the Nile created one of the world's greatest civilizations in ancient Egypt. The value of the old system of canals and channels is evident today, in this view of the delta near Cairo, where the darkness of vegetation contrasts with the pale desert sands in a sharply drawn line.

NASA

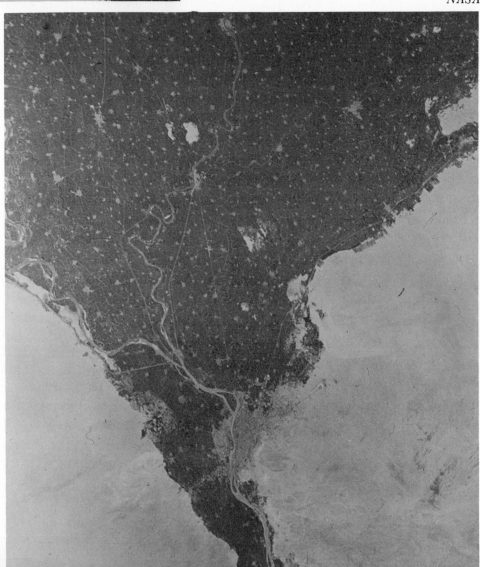

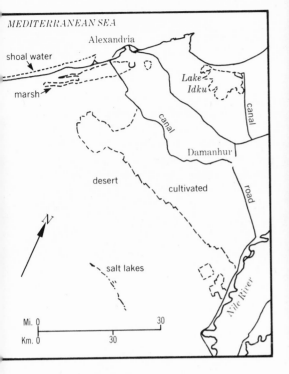

Wonders of the ancient, and modern, world — the Pyramids — are in Giza, across the Nile from Cairo. The Pyramid of Khufu (or Cheops), the largest and oldest, lies between the Pyramid of Kharfe (left) and that of Menkure. All were built between 2870 and 2800 B.C. The Sphinx, seen here from the rear, is at the upper right in the photograph.

Aerofilms, Ltd.

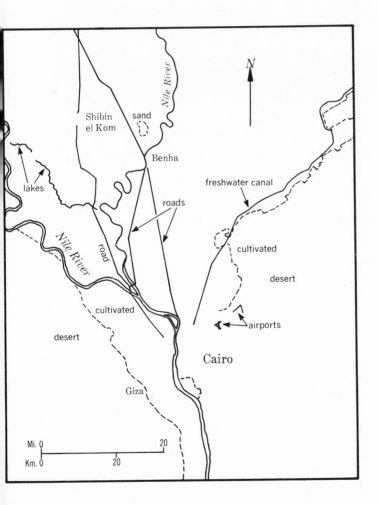

a project completed by Darius and Xerxes; redug by Ptolemy II and Trajan, and was in use until the eighth century. Today the route, visible in the Gemini photographs, is used by the Sweetwater Canal, which provides freshwater to the area.

Geologically the U.A.R. is part of the desert that stretches from the Atlantic Ocean to Pakistan and India. The Red Sea is evidence of crustal separation, which was recently emphasized by the discovery of deep "hot spots" where the water temperature is 1-1/2 times that of water at the surface. Some oceanographers believe this heat flows from the interior of the earth in a fashion thought to have ended a thousand million years ago anywhere on earth.

West of the Nile the desert is an arid, treeless plain made up of limestone, and sandstone. East of the river lies a rugged highland zone of limestone with some sandstone and rocks of the basement complex. The Sinai Peninsula is largely plateau and plain, with Jebel Katherina (Mount Sinai) dominating the mountains in the south.

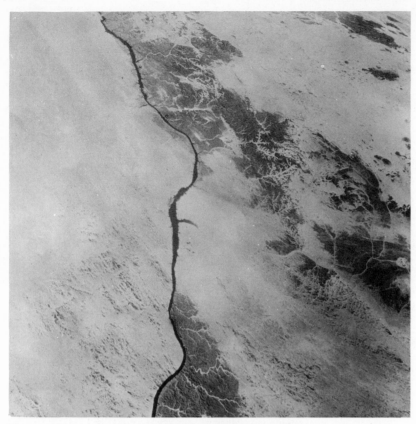

Upstream from the Aswan High Dam, the Nile waters are impounded for flood control and hydroelectric power. When this Gemini 4 photograph was taken, the reservoir was beginning to fill, as is evident in the side canyons with water in them. This dam is the latest in a series, including an earlier Aswan Dam still in use farther downstream, built to control the Nile.

NASA

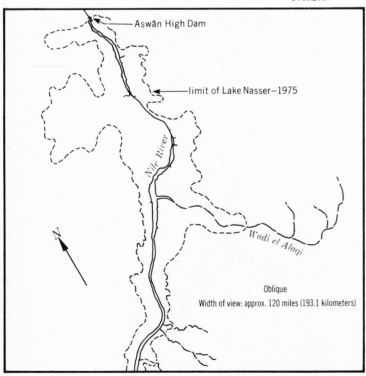

Aswān High Dam

limit of Lake Nasser—1975

Nile River

N

Wadi el Alaqi

Oblique
Width of view: approx. 120 miles (193.1 kilometers)

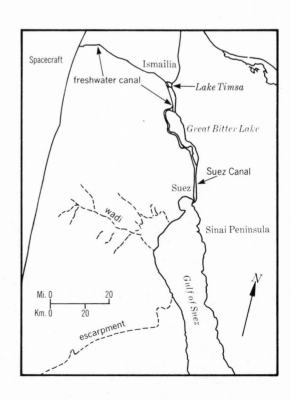

Spacecraft

Ismailia

freshwater canal

Lake Timsa

Great Bitter Lake

Suez Canal

Suez

wadi

Sinai Peninsula

Gulf of Suez

Mi. 0   20

Km. 0   20

escarpment

N

Centuries of drifting sand have filled the Gulf of Suez from Lake Timsah south, since the earliest canal connected the Nile and Gulf. Used to carry fresh water today, the ancient canal route is defined by the line of vegetation at the upper left. Some of the route of the modern Suez Canal is visible as a straight line.

NASA

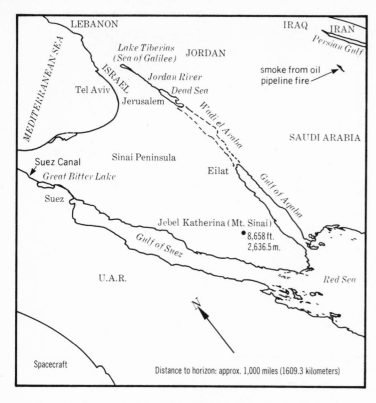

LEBANON

MEDITERRANEAN SEA

Lake Tiberias (Sea of Galilee) JORDAN

IRAQ IRAN
Persian Gulf

smoke from oil
pipeline fire →

ISRAEL *Jordan River*
Dead Sea

Tel Aviv
Jerusalem

Wadi el Aqaba

SAUDI ARABIA

Suez Canal
Great Bitter Lake

Sinai Peninsula

Eilat

Gulf of Aqaba

Suez

Jebel Katherina (Mt. Sinai)
● 8,658 ft.
2,636.5 m.

Gulf of Suez

N

U.A.R.

Red Sea

Spacecraft

Distance to horizon: approx. 1,000 miles (1609.3 kilometers)

Israel
Jordan

The rift valley Wadi el Araba is the below-sea-level depression forming a part-geological and part-political boundary between Israel and Jordan. At the lowest part of the wadi lies the Dead Sea, which drains the Jordan River valley. The river rises in the Anti-Lebanon (Jebel esh Shargi) Mountains and meanders down the narrow valley

The rift valley defile of Wadi el-Araba can easily be traced in this Gemini 11 photograph up the Gulf of Aqaba to the Dead Sea, and beyond. At the upper right a tiny dark triangle in the desert area is smoke from an oil pipeline fire. The photograph also covers many of the religious and historic centers of Christianity, Islam, and Judaism.

NASA

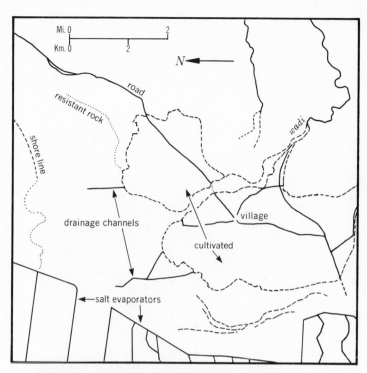

from the Lake of Tiberias or Yam Kinneret (Sea of Galilee). The shores of the Dead Sea are the lowest spot on the surface of the earth.

On a broader scale, the Wadi el Araba and Gulf of Aqaba are a fault zone on one flank of the Arabian Peninsula which is moving northward away from Africa. The Red Sea and Gulf of Aden now fill the gap between two crustal blocks.

Measurement of the movement of the Wadi el Araba shows a total displacement between the east and west sides of the valley of over 66 miles (106 kilometers).

Economically, the valley is of value for the water from the Jordan and the salt that is extracted from the Dead Sea by natural evaporation.

Economic utilization of the Dead Sea is limited, as its waters are far too saline to support fish. Brine, evaporated in diked pans, is one of the few industries. A region of salt-gathering and small farming near a single village are visible in this view of the Jordan shore.

Fairey Surveys, Ltd.

Volcanic islands, such as the Canary and Cape Verde Islands, are indicative of the turbulent forces present in the "living" crust of the earth. These peaks jut up from the abyssal plain depths of the ocean floor. The highest peak in the Canaries is more than 28,000 feet (8,534 meters) above the average depth of the plain.

NASA

CANARY ISLANDS

CAPE VERDE ISLANDS

Both island groups are volcanic peaks rising steeply from the ocean depths, and have no underwater "bridge" to the continent. The highest peak in the Canary Islands is 28,198 feet (8,593.6 meters) above the average depth of the deep sea abyssal plains, and the height of the Cape Verde Island peaks is nearly the same. In effect, these volcanic cones are of the same dimensions as the Himalayan peaks.

Oceanic volcanoes are of interest to geologists because most of them seem to form away from the midocean ridge system. The Canary and Cape Verde Islands offer geologists a chance to examine "growing" land at close hand.

Volcanic islands that push their way above the surface of the sea are less common than the seamounts and guyots (flat-topped seamounts) found throughout the world's oceans. Seamounts are volcanic peaks that grew too slowly or were eroded as they were being built.

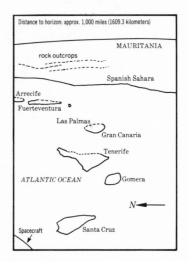

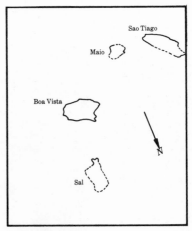

Mauritania
Senegal
The Gambia

The desert merges with the tropical coastal plain at the Senegal River in West Africa. Dakar, the principal port on the outer bulge of Africa, is an artificial harbor built in the lee of the Cape Verde peninsula. Use of Sengal river waters for irrigation and reclamation has been made through the Richard Toll scheme. The project's holding reservoirs show as arms of the Senegal River.

NASA

The southern edge of the Sahara is one of the most sharply defined geographical boundaries in the world. At about the latitude of the Cape Verde Islands and the mouth of the Senegal River, a nearly straight west-to-east line could be drawn separating the desert from tropical lands to the south. Every aspect of geography, including rainfall, vegetation, population, and prevailing winds, finds this latitude a natural barrier.

Mauritania, north of the Senegal River, is largely desert, with important iron and copper deposits in the ancient rocks of the interior. Some of the oldest rocks in the world have been exposed by erosion to jut up as cliffs in the desert

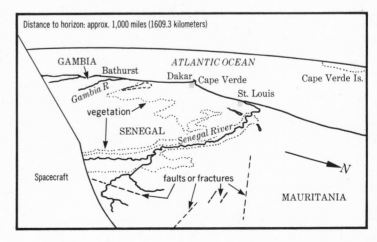

Distance to horizon: approx. 1,000 miles (1609.3 kilometers)

GAMBIA
Bathurst
ATLANTIC OCEAN
Dakar Cape Verde
Cape Verde Is.
Gambia R.
St. Louis
vegetation
SENEGAL
Senegal River
Spacecraft
faults or fractures
N
MAURITANIA

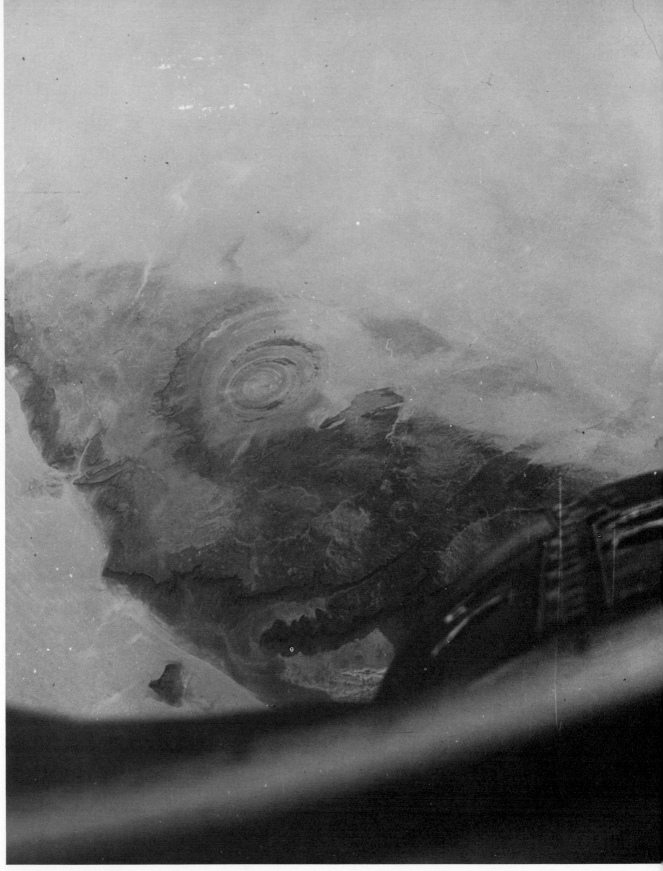

In western Mauritania the Richat structures have aroused considerable interest among geologists. These depressions may be meteorite impact sites or eroded domes, forced upward in sedimentary rocks by intrusive molten material.

NASA

sands. In Mauritania, the circular Richat structures, photographed during almost every astronauts' flight, are one of the most striking geologic features in the world. French geologic studies, noting that the formations are in sedimentary rock, suggest that the concentric rings of the larger structure are part of an eroded dome. Other geologists feel the phenomenon may be due to meteorite impact.

Nouakchott, the capital of Mauritania, was a small village on the Atlantic coast when independence was achieved in 1958. By 1968 it had grown to a population of 35,000 as the seat of government of an area about four-fifths the size of Alaska.

Senegal lies in a geographical transition zone between the very dry desert north of the Senegal River and the excessively wet region immediately south of the country. The Senegal River is seasonally navigable in Senegal for vessels of shallow draft. Dakar is the largest city in western Africa (population 374,000) and has been a port since the 1850's. The airport at Dakar has been a landfall for transatlantic flights for many years. Today the city is a cosmopolitan community whose beaches have become an international resort.

The tiny republic of The Gambia is a small formerly British incursion into what was once part of French West Africa. Gambia is the smallest country on the continent and essentially is a narrow strip of territory along both banks of the Gambia River. Like Senegal, it is a black Moslem country but with an important minority of West Indian immigrants.

In the history of Africa, Mauritania, Senegal, and Gambia played a part in the slave trade, although less of a role than equatorial Africa. Slavery began, and is still continued in some places by Arabs and Africans, as a commercial trade. Ancient societies had slaves but they were usually captured enemies or the poorer members of society. From the sixteenth to nineteenth centuries, slaves were the chief export of the continent.

With the abolition of slavery in Great Britain in 1772, and in the United States in 1865, suppression of the slave trade became national policy in Europe and the United States. Freetown and Bathurst, the principal cities of Gambia, were established as landing places for slaves freed from captured ships. St. Louis, second largest city in Senegal, had a large community of former slaves.

A byproduct of the slave trade was the introduction in Africa of food products from the Americas or Asia by Portuguese slavers. Cassava, sweet potatoes, peanuts, corn, and lima

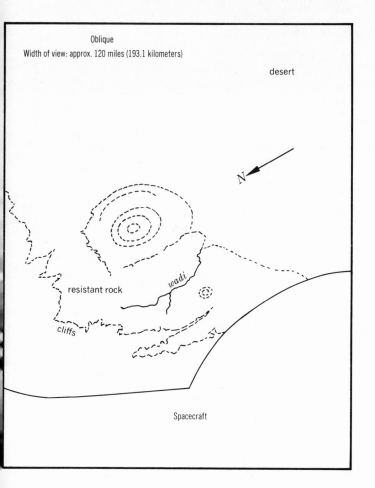

Oblique
Width of view: approx. 120 miles (193.1 kilometers)

desert

N

resistant rock

wadi

cliffs

Spacecraft

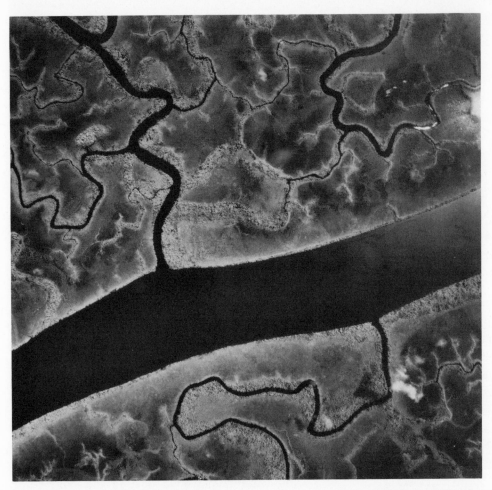

Land-building along low-lying tropical river shores often stems from floating forests of mangrove. Silt and debris collect in the roots of this tree that grows in salt water, and gradually soil begins to form. Unfortunately, mangrove can invade valuable land by intrusion, as is happening in southern Florida in the United States. This photograph shows a swamp in Gambia.

Fairey Surveys, Ltd.

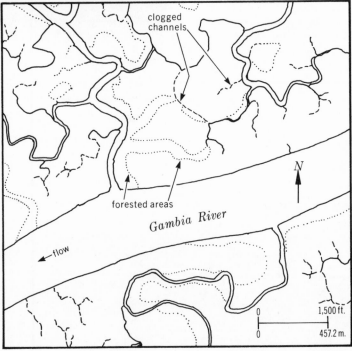

beans came from the New World; yams, bananas, beans, peas, and sugarcane came from Asia. Today, peanuts are the principal crop of Gambia and are an important commodity in Senegal.

Increased industrialization throughout this part of Africa is currently based on phosphate and titanium in Senegal, previously mentioned iron and copper in Mauritania, and some petroleum. Senegal has established the region's first cement factory near Dakar.

154

An unusual internal delta on the Niger River near Timbuktu, Mali, promises to be a source of arable land. Parts of the delta are in old, stablized chains of sand dunes. The linear quality of part of the Niger flood pattern is evident in the photograph.

NASA

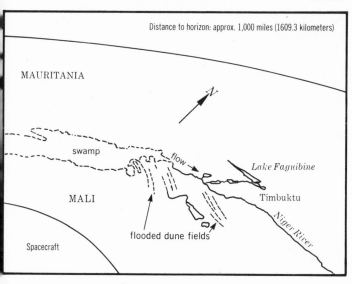

Distance to horizon: approx. 1,000 miles (1609.3 kilometers)

MAURITANIA

N

swamp

flow

Lake Faguibine

MALI

Timbuktu

flooded dune fields

Niger River

Spacecraft

Mali

Mali is a historical center of Islam whose second largest city, Timbuktu (Tombouctou), served as a symbol of remoteness for many years. Today the city is still a caravan junction, but it is also a tourist stop served by the national airline. Bamako, on the lower Niger River, is the capital of Mali.

The El Juf of Taoudene region, shown in the accompanying photograph, is a vast depression in the southern Sahara. To the south lies the Niger River, whose great bend in Mali forms a 30,000-square-mile (77,700-square-kilometer) region of river channels and marsh. The drainage pattern of this part of the river is so complex it is termed either an interior or fossil delta. The upper Niger once drained into the desert sands, but the river was captured, as geologists term it, by the lower Niger when this river cut its way upstream into the upper-river drainage system.

155

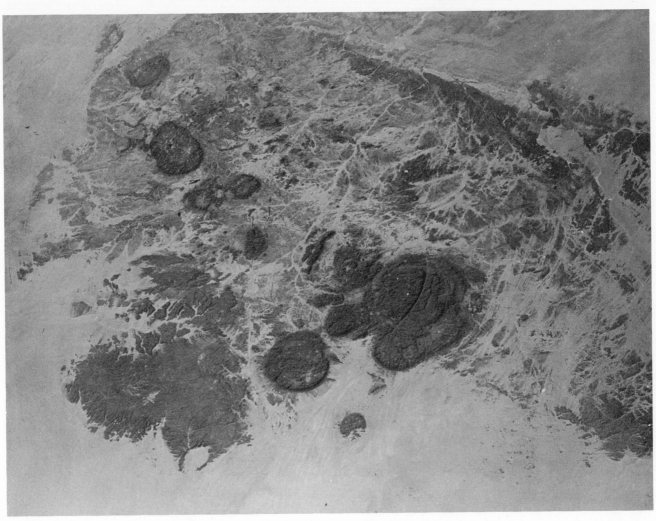

Some of the oldest rocks in the world are shown in this photograph of the Aïr ou Azbine uplift in Niger. The generally circular igneous intrusions were molten more than 500 million years ago. Over the millenniums the rocks of the Aïr have been fractured and eroded, but preserve a once-liquid appearance.

NASA

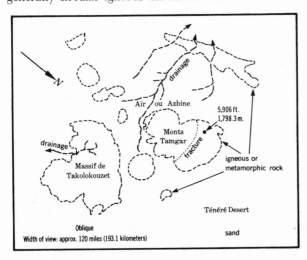

Niger

Of the landlocked countries of Africa, Niger has the fewest developed natural resources, and agriculture is dependent on the seasonal floods of the Niger River valley, which cuts across a narrow neck of the country. Most of the Nigerian economy depends on livestock kept and traded by the Tuareg, a nomadic people of the Sahara.

In the center of Niger, the Aïr ou Azbine is a region of rugged uplift where lava juts above the sand. Several tin mines, thermal springs, and a few palm groves line ancient caravan routes in the area.

Aerial photography, the only practicable survey method in so inhospitable a region, is being used for soil survey maps and other cartography as part of a national development scheme in Niger.

156

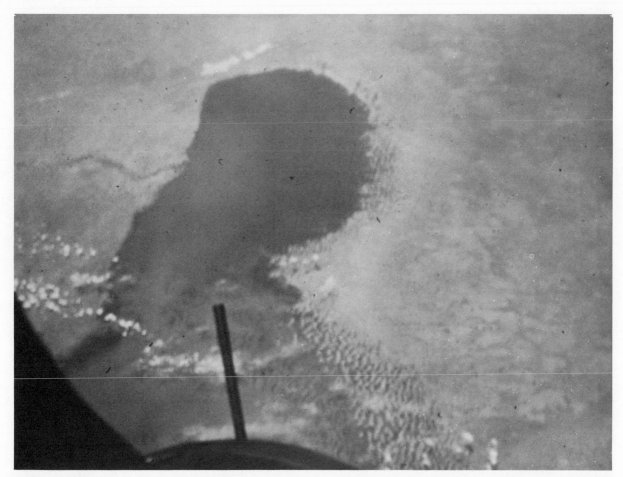

Agricultural development of the southern Sahara has reached its greatest advance in the reclamation of part of Lake Chad. The lake straddles the borders of four nations: Niger, Chad, Cameroon, and Nigeria. Under United Nations auspices, reclaimed polder yielded crops a few years after creation of the new land. As with the interior Niger River delta, Lake Chad inundates dune fields.

NASA

Chad

Lake Chad is an important natural resource of the southern Sahara. Slightly smaller than Lake Ontario, Lake Chad lies in an enclosed basin with no visible outlet. Despite this, the lake water is not stagnant, and drains underground to provide water to oases as far as 450 miles (724.2 kilometers) to the north.

The lake basin is in four countries, and an international reclamation scheme, under United Nations auspices, began early in the 1960's. The first polder, reclaimed in 1966, already produces grain in economic quantities.

Water drains into the lake from a range of hills in the neighboring Central African Republic. Uplift of these hills probably diverted water into Lake Chad that would have flowed seaward via the Ubangi and Congo rivers.

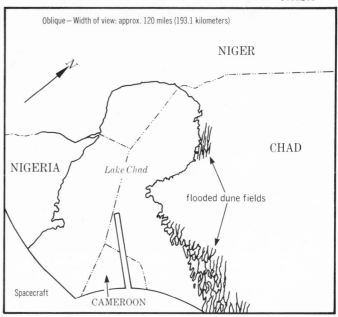

Oblique — Width of view: approx. 120 miles (193.1 kilometers)

NIGER

CHAD

NIGERIA

Lake Chad

flooded dune fields

Spacecraft

CAMEROON

157

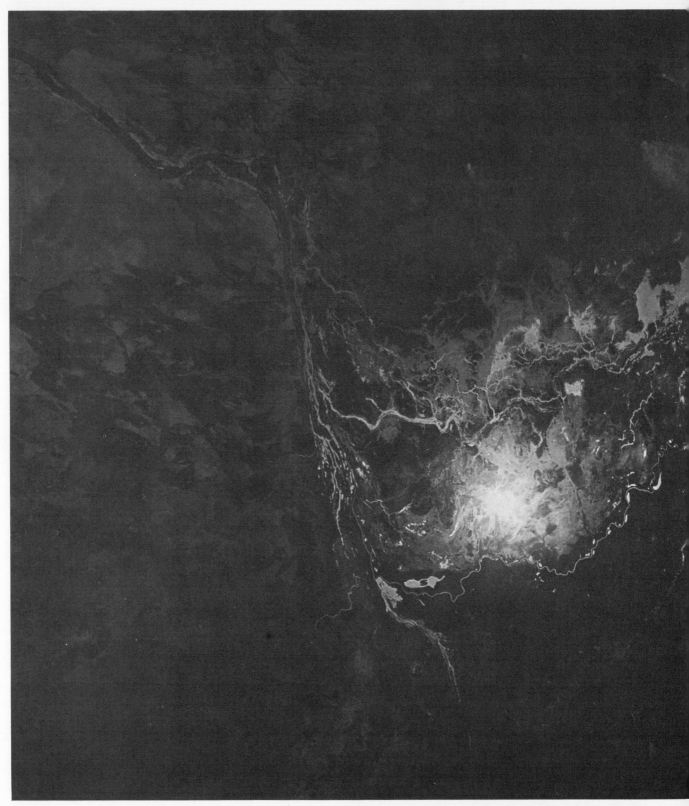

The upper reaches of the White Nile (Bahr el-Jebel) drain the bottom of a former lake. An immense swamp called the Sudd was created when the lake overflowed as the land rose. Although the Nile is navigable as it passes through the Sudd, masses of floating vegetation hamper use of the swamp for agriculture.

NASA

Sudan

The name Sudan, used for the political entity of today, is also a geographical term that includes parts of Sudan, Chad, and Ethiopia. The name is also used to identify the entire southern Sahara. The reason for this broad usage is in the original Arabic name Bilad-es-Sudan, which means Country of the Blacks.

Sudan is the largest country in Africa, and extends from the tropics in the south to the desert in the north. Physically, the country is a plain whose vegetation is dependent on latitude. The Nile River, which bisects Sudan, is a principal natural resource.

The Nile has two main tributaries, which meet at Khartoum, the national capital. The White Nile branch drains Lake Albert and Lake Victoria but loses half of its water in the great Sudd swamp. The Blue Nile rises in the highlands of Ethiopia, and provides most of the water for the lower Nile in Sudan and the U.A.R.

The Sudd is a permanent swamp in the bottom of an ancient lake that overflowed to create the White Nile.

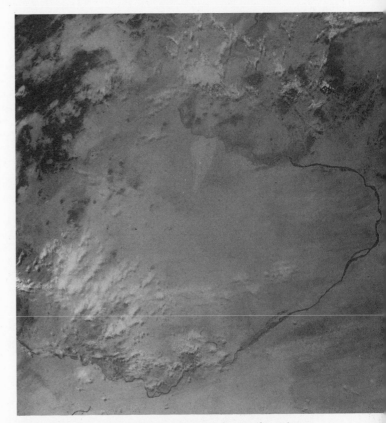

As it cuts its way through the rock and dunes of northern Sudan, the Nile River makes an S-curve known as the Great Bend. Cataracts or rapids on the river have been landmarks since settlement by Egyptians under the Pharaohs. Archaeological sites line the riverbank. Near the Red Sea shore, visible in the photograph, the land is tipped up in a series of formidable ridges.

NASA

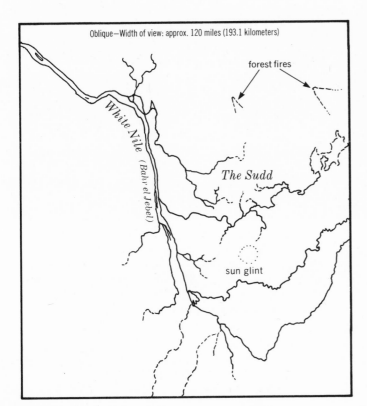

Oblique—Width of view: approx. 120 miles (193.1 kilometers)

forest fires

White Nile (Bahr el Jebel)

The Sudd

sun glint

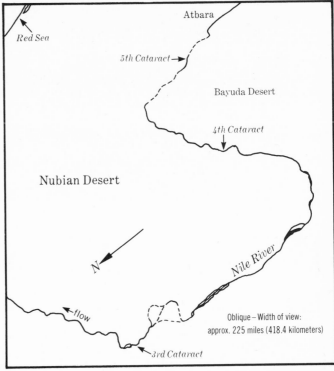

Red Sea

Atbara

5th Cataract

Bayuda Desert

4th Cataract

Nubian Desert

N

Nile River

flow

Oblique – Width of view: approx. 225 miles (418.4 kilometers)

3rd Cataract

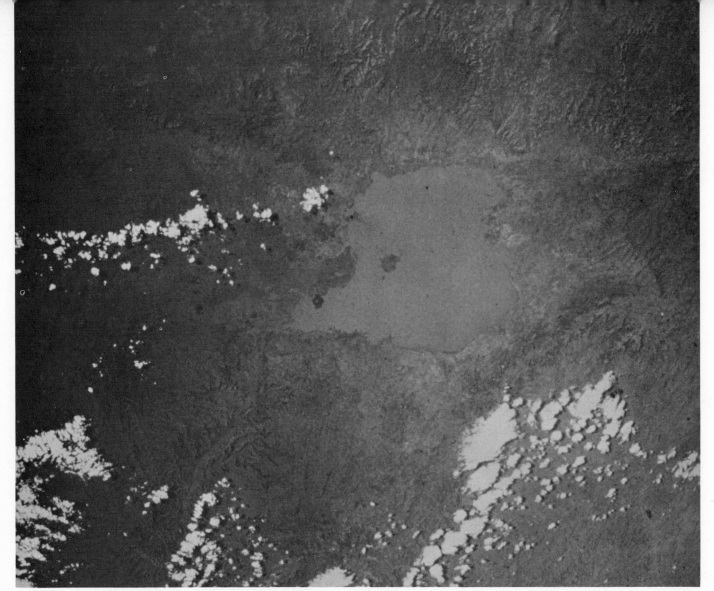

The chief source of water for the Nile River is Lake Tana, Ethiopia, part of the Blue Nile. This lake lies high in the western segment of the plateau covering most of the country. A monastery on an island in the lake, and other religious establishments nearby, are part of the Coptic Christian Church.

NASA

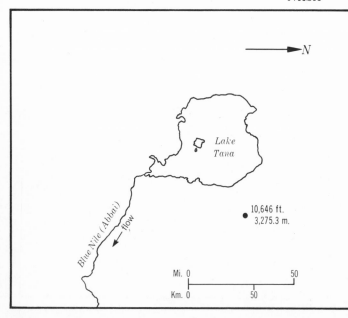

Ethiopia
Somalia

Most of Ethiopia is a high plateau bisected by the gorge of a rift valley. The valley widens as it reaches the Red Sea and Gulf of Aden. There, complex structures of plain, horst, and graben conceal the essential parallelism of the Red Sea as it narrows through the Straits of Bab el-Maneb. The gradual widening of the Gulf of Aden has been interpreted to mean that the Arabian peninsula has swung slightly anti-clockwise relative to Africa.

Lake Tana, in the western Ethiopian plateau, is the source of the Blue Nile. This region is the highest populated area of the world outside the Himalayas and the Andes. In descending from the highlands the river, known in Ethiopia as the Abbai River, cuts a 6,000-doot (1,828.8-meter)

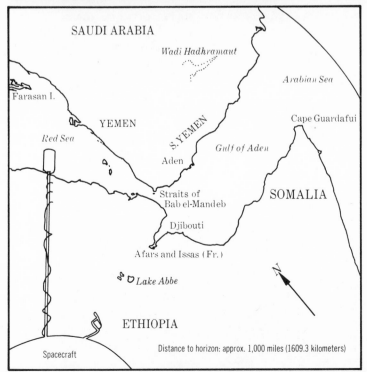

SAUDI ARABIA

Wadi Hadhramaut

Arabian Sea

Farasan I.

YEMEN

S. YEMEN

Cape Guardafui

Red Sea

Gulf of Aden

Aden

Straits of
Bab el-Mandeb

SOMALIA

Djibouti

Afars and Issas (Fr.)

Lake Abbe

N

ETHIOPIA

Spacecraft   Distance to horizon: approx. 1,000 miles (1609.3 kilometers)

Africa and Asia are separated by the Straits of Bab el-Mandeb, where the Red Sea widens into the Gulf of Aden, a part of the Indian Ocean.   *NASA*

deep gorge, and makes a 360-degree loop before it joins the White Nile at Khartoum.

Somalia is a coastal country along the African shore of the Gulf of Aden and the Indian Ocean. The dry northwestern plain or *guban* (meaning "burnt") is noted chiefly for its frankincense and myrrh trees, whose Islamic owners provide nine-tenths of the incense used in Christian rituals.

To geologists, the sinking blocks of the rift valleys and the heated rock below the Red Sea are two separate elements of continental drift. The rifts are breaks in the crust, and the heated sea floor is indicative of sea-floor spreading where new crustal material forms as the oceans widen.

161

Lake
Mweru

ZAMBIA

REPUBLIC OF THE CONGO

N

Lake Tanganyika

TANZANIA

Kenya Tanzania Malawai

The dominant geographical feature of eastern Africa is the rift valley system — a related series of long, narrow depressed segments of the earth's crust that extend more than 1,800 miles (2,896.8 kilometers) from the Zambezi River gorge in Mozambique to the Red Sea.

Some of the fault scarps are over 270 million years old, as determined by the exposed rocks. But there was an important active phase in the rift system between 25 and 12 million years ago, with some activity still continuing. Associated with the rift valleys are a number of volcanoes and lava fields, an indication that the rifts are an active part of the earth's crust directly connected

Lake Tanganyika is the largest of several lakes filling segments of the great rift valley system of Africa. The bottom of the lake is 2,150 feet (655.3 meters) below sea level, while the surface is 2,535 feet (773 meters) above sea level. The dimensions of the rift demonstrate the size of elements of continental drift.   *NASA*

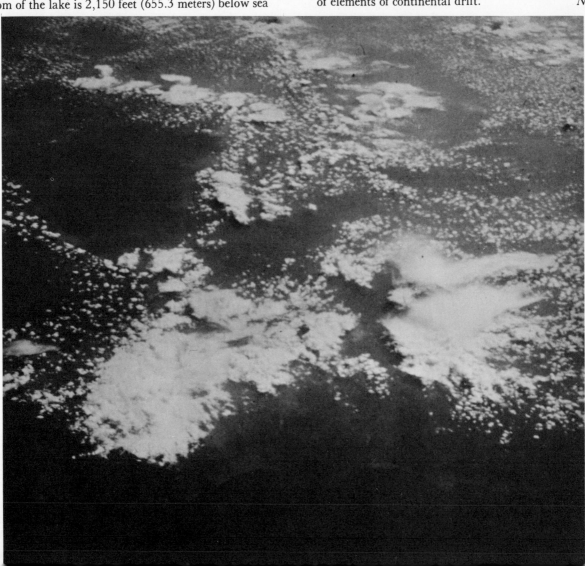

with the molten interior. The width of the valleys (between about 25 to 35 miles or 40 to 60 kilometers) is about the same as the thickness of the earth's crust below the rift, a definite relationship proved by laboratory experiments with scale models.

The African rift system is outlined by a series of long narrow lakes filling some of the valleys. Lake Rudolf is the only large lake in the eastern rift, but the western valley is filled by a chain of lakes, including Lake Tanganyika and Lake Malawi. In between the semicircular pattern of the valleys is an uplifted plateau, raised as the rifts were depressed. Lake Victoria fills part of a shallow depression in the plateau.

The general acceptance of the continental-drift concept by the scientific community is barely ten years old. One area of disagreement is the fitting together of the southern landmass Gondwanaland and the relationship between the east coast

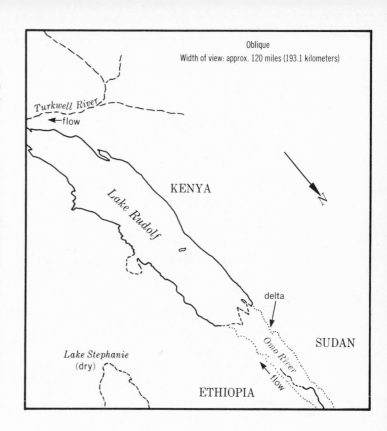

The principal lake in the eastern section of the rift, Lake Rudolf, fills the lower portion of a valley rather than the entire valley as does Lake Tanganyika. Its name is one of the few on the continent recalling the period of German colonialism before 1918.

NASA

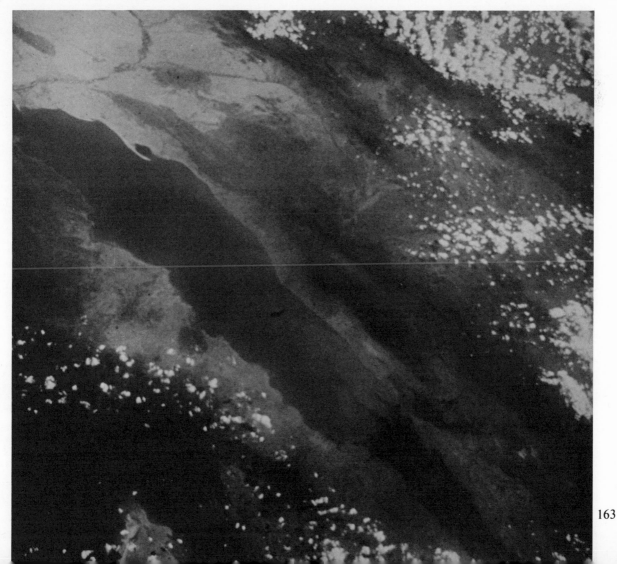

of Africa, India, and Antarctica and Australia before the proto-continent opened up, beginning about 225 million years ago. Some of the answers lie in the rocks and sediments of the spreading sea floor. Other answers will be found in the deeping rifts of East Africa.

The chief benefit of local geology to the people of East Africa is partly in the vast water supply of the lakes and also in the moderate climate compared to the constant heat of the lowlands. Kenya is the largest producer of tea in Africa, and coffee is the leading cash crop. Malawi produces tobacco, coffee, cotton, and tung oil (used in varnishes), and has considerable forest lands. Although the coastal segment of Tanzania is most famous for its cloves (80 percent of the world supply) and other tropical agricultural products, the highland interiors are forested, and are also a source of salt, sodas, and other commercially valuable chemicals.

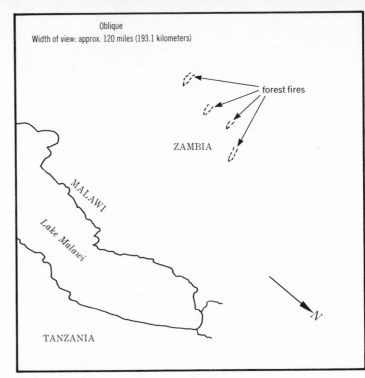

The most southerly of the rift valley great lakes is Lake Malawi, formerly Lake Nyasa. Only slightly smaller than Lake Tanganyika, Lake Malawi fills a fork of the rift leading toward the Indian Ocean. The inland segment of the valley is traversed by the Luangwa River, a tributary of the Zambesi.   *NASA*

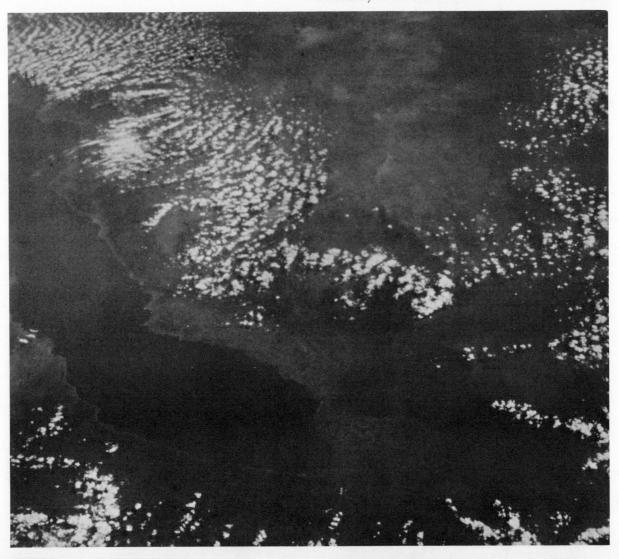

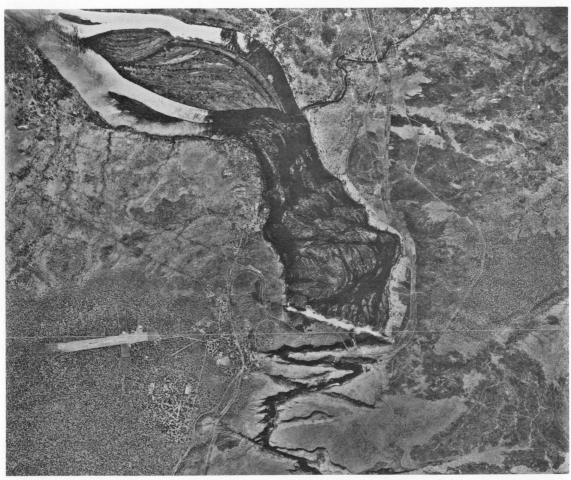

Rhodesia
Zambia

Victoria Falls, one of the great waterfalls of the world, is a scenic attraction on the upper Zambezi River. An indication of the erosive power of the river is that it has cut back through eighty miles (128.7 kilometers) of nearly solid crystalline rock in the past 300 million years. The falls are 360 feet (109.7 meters) high at low water and 1-1/4 of a mile (2 kilometers) across. One striking feature of the falls is the zigzag shape of the gorge. Here the river has cut along lines of structural weakness in the rock masses that are traceable in the accompanying aerial view.

Both Rhodesia and Zambia are rich in mineral resources, particularly copper. Zambia ranks third in world production of the mineral. Rhodesia has a greater variety of other metals, especially gold. Some of the Rhodesian gold mines were worked long before the arrival of European settlers.

Victoria Falls, on the Zambezi River, is an excellent example of the relationship between the land and its structure and the power of a river. The falls themselves define a fracture that extends some distance to the side of the river. The series of zigzags of the gorge locate earlier positions of the falls. Dr. David Livingstone discovered the falls in 1855.

Fairey Surveys, Ltd.

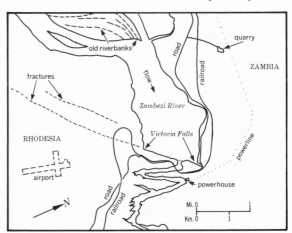

Tropical east Africa, with its Arab, Indo-Pakistani, and Indonesian influences, has been a source of spices for Egypt, Arabia, and Europe for over 4,000 years. Both

Mozambique and Malagasy, with Zanzibar and Pemba Islands, are fertile lands whose vanilla, cloves, and resins still supply most of the world's needs.   *NASA*

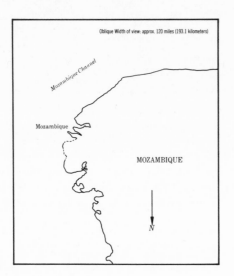

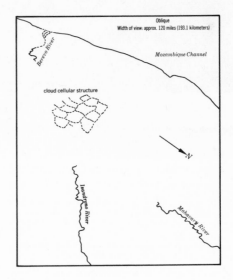

Mozambique Malagasy

Mozambique and Malagasy (which occupies the island of Madagascar) are separated by the Mozambique Channel. The coastal communities along the channel have been ports of call for thousands of years as traders from Africa, India, and Arabia used the winter monsoon winds to sail southward.

Madagascar Island was once part of continental Africa, and drifted southeastward when this

part of Gondwanaland opened up. Most of the rocks of both Mozambique and Malagasy are between 700 and 450 million years old. Later, predrift tropical climates produced the coal beds found in both countries today.

The accompanying photographs are consecutive pictures, and show typical patterns of cumulus-cloud development. In the view of Mozambique, the cotton-boll-like clouds have coalesced into larger cells, and from the ground the sky would appear overcast. In the view of Malagasy, the development is similar but not so far advanced toward a large cloud mass.

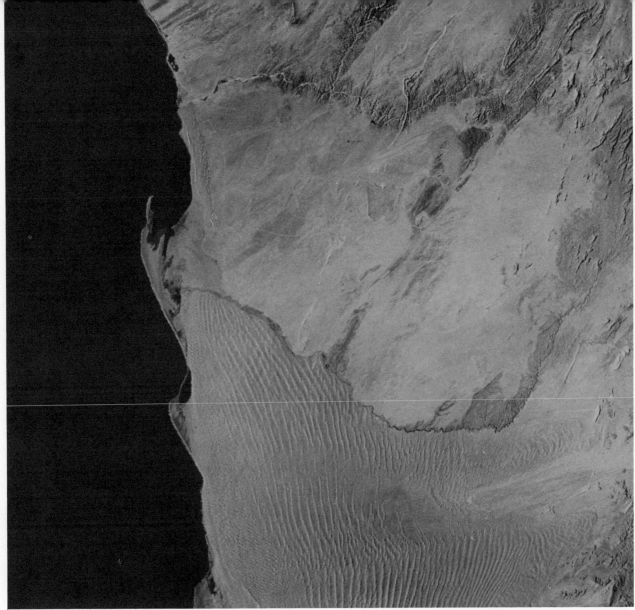

The coast of Southwest Africa is similar to the Atlantic shore of Morocco and Mauritania in its deserts and mountains. However, the eroded ridges of the south are from 600 to 850 million years old, about twice the age of the Anti-Atlas mountains. Along the shore the north-flowing Benguela current influences the topography as it builds and shapes a series of capes, shown in the photo.

NASA

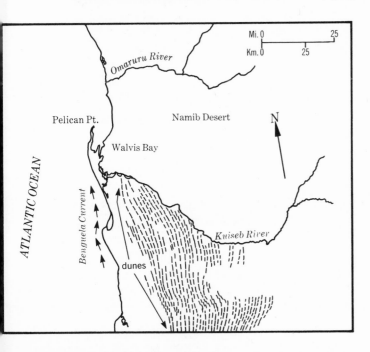

South-West Africa (Namibia)

Nominally a trusteeship territory of South Africa under a mandate originally established by the League of Nations, South-West Africa is essentially an associate state of South Africa, with Walvis Bay a separate territorial unit of South Africa. A United Nations resolution in 1968 called for UN administration of South-West Africa, and renamed it Namibia. But South Africa has refused to yield its suzerainty.

As the accompanying aerial photographs show, the region is desolate and rugged. Along

167

The complexities of geology are ably illustrated by this and the following Gemini photographs of southern Africa. This region, part of the protocontinent Gondwanaland, is composed of very old rocks, some of which were formed over 2,000 million years ago. Folding, or lack of it, and erosion combined with glaciation and a present dry climate to produce rugged, bare terrain.

NASA

the shore, the Namib Desert is called the Skeleton Coast by mariners who dread shipwreck on the waterless wastes. The dune fields south of the Kuiseb River are the largest south of the Sahara.

Geologically, the region is quite complex. Although an anticline and other folded mountain features are prominent, they are ancient metamorphic rock rather than near-surface sediments of recent geologic time. Some of the features seem to be fractured by erosion, an indication of crystalline rocks.

Along the coast the north-flowing Benguela Current has created Pelican Point and Sandwich Head and barrier islands. These sandspits are following classical lines of development, but the tremendous amount of sand caused by winds blowing off the desert has created features of considerable size.

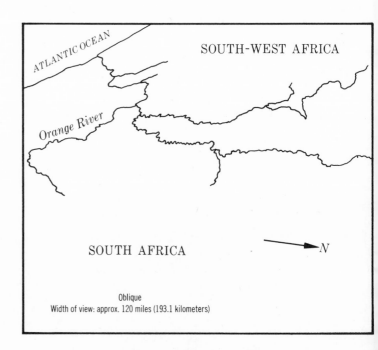

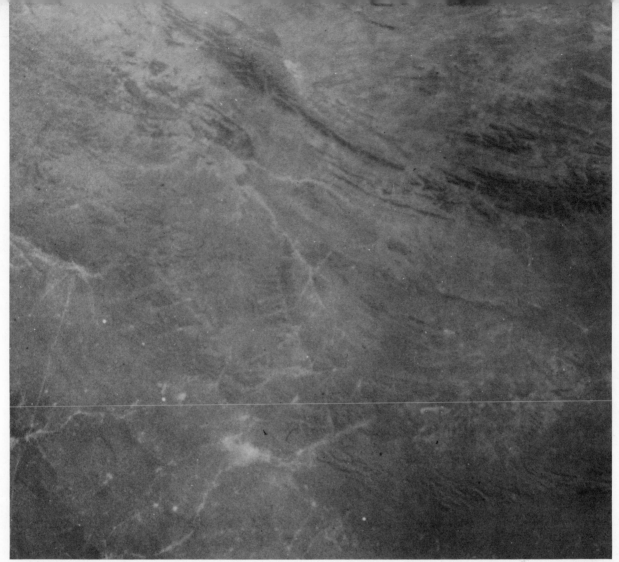

Some of the richest concentrations of precious and base minerals in the world lie in the sedimentary folds, granitic intrusions, and volcanic diamond pipes of South Africa. Yet other sections are pieces of Gondwanaland preserved nearly intact for about 140 million years. Uplift, erosion, vulcanism, and intrusion combined to create the vast resources of South Africa in a great natural "crucible."   *NASA*

South Africa

One of the most striking features of South Africa's geology is the antiquity of the rocks — some have been dated back well over 2,000 million years — and the tremendous age difference between the country's geographical features.

Some of the original Gondwanaland surface remains over large areas. This surface has been largely undisturbed for the past 140 million years when it was molten lava. Elsewhere, several river systems have eroded mountains of sediment to expose the ancient "bedrock."

South Africa is the world leader in production of gold, gem diamonds, platinum, and antimony. It is second or third in chrome, uranium, manganese, asbestos, and other metals. In addition, South Africa has unlimited coal and iron deposits.

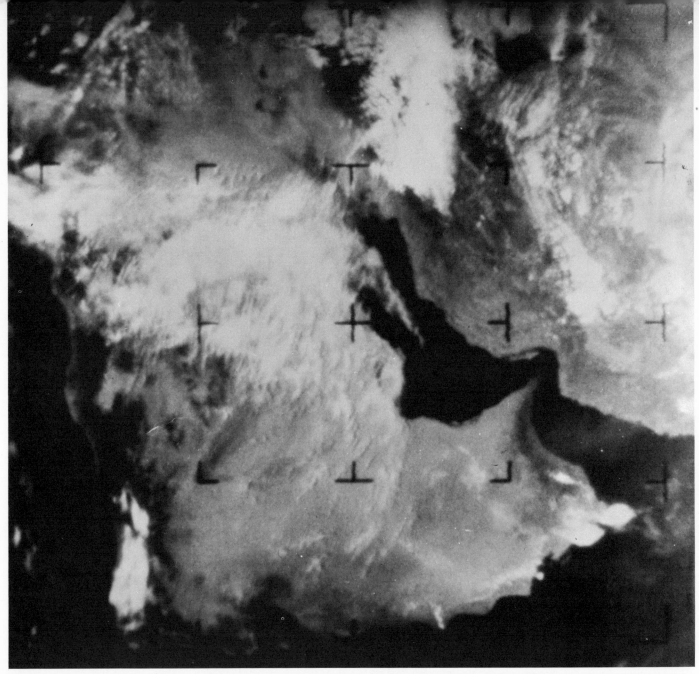

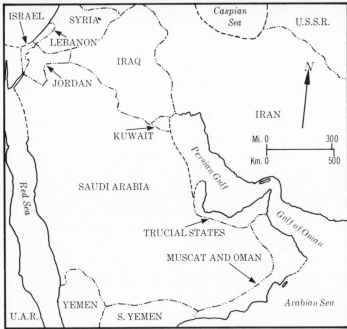

The Arabian peninsula is a pivoting land mass, moving away from Africa as the Red Sea widens and Persian Gulf closes. The mountains of Muscat and Oman are geologically part of Iran across the Gulf. Most of the peninsula is a geological segment of Africa.

NASA

Part VI
ASIA

The continent of Asia forms the major part of Eurasia, the world's largest land mass. Asia itself is nearly twice the size of North America. With the associated islands of Indonesia, the continent extends from the Arctic Ocean to south of the equator, encompassing nearly one-quarter of the globe. Geographically the continent ranges from great desert basins to shoal tropic waters to the highest mountain range in the world — the Himalayas.

Asia once formed most of Laurasia, the great pre-continental land mass of the Northern Hemisphere. The subcontinent of India was then part of Gondwanaland, the landmass of the Southern Hemisphere.*

In the U.S.S.R., which covers the entire northern half of the continent, Asia is considered to begin east of the north-south Ural Mountain range.

More than half the world's population lives in Asia. Cultural links with some of man's earliest civilizations have sometimes led to centuries-old agricultural practices, visible in aerial photographs. In other cases only the relics remain of once-mighty nations.

As the older societies of Asia develop — or perhaps redevelop — in the current Age of Technology, aerial photography is playing an important role. Surveys and maps made from aerial photographs are a prime source of data used in the first steps of this new era.

In this section of the atlas, aerial, astronaut, and satellite photographs show some of the characteristics of the vast continent and of man's impress over thousands of years of occupation.

*"Laur" is a geographic suffic used in Canada for such names as Laurentian. "Gondwana" has as its root a reference to an eighteenth-century Indian kingdom, and its people the Gond.

In this view across Cyprus and Turkey, part of the much-folded edge of the proto-continent Laurasia is visible. Although erosion has altered the surface, earthquakes in the area indicated the tensions built up in the crustal plate. The dark Troodos Massif of Cyprus is material uplifted from beneath the earth's crust.

NASA

Turkey

Geographically, Turkey projects toward Europe as a "peninsula" lying between the Black and Mediterranean seas. Called Asia Minor, this region is mostly occupied by modern Turkey whose Dardanelles, Sea of Marmara, and Bosporus form a waterway linking the Black Sea with the Mediterranean. The country is extremely complex geographically, with a topography to match.

In the south the sinuous chain of the Taurus Mountains (Toros Daglari) reach heights of 11,000 feet (3,352.8 meters). The interior is a rugged, high plateau with several extinct volcanoes and basins having internal drainage.

Nearby, in the Mediterranean, is the island of Cyprus, whose Troodos Massif mountains are possibly a wedge of the subcrustal mantle forced up and over the edge of the crust underlying Africa, when the ancient Tethys Sea closed up.

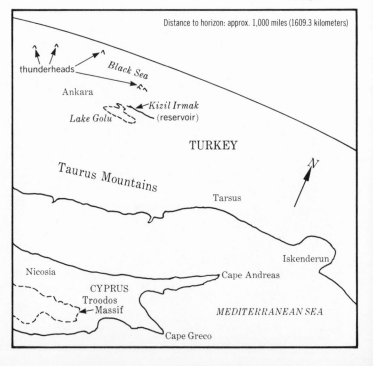

Distance to horizon: approx. 1,000 miles (1609.3 kilometers)

thunderheads
Black Sea
Ankara
Kizil Irmak
(reservoir)
Lake Golu

TURKEY

N

Taurus Mountains

Tarsus

Iskenderun

Nicosia
Cape Andreas

CYPRUS
Troodos
Massif

MEDITERRANEAN SEA

Cape Greco

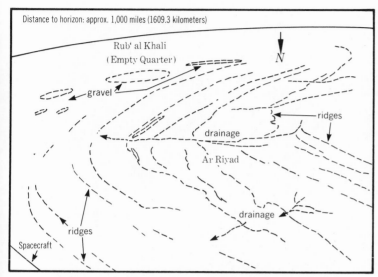

Rub' al Khali
(Empty Quarter)

N

gravel

ridges

drainage

Ar Riyad

drainage

ridges

Spacecraft

The arcing ranges of Jabal Tuwayq in central Saudi Arabia are the edges of great layers of sedimentary beds. A wind and water gap through the mountains provides access to the Persian (or Arabian) Gulf. Ar Riyad is the national capital. A nearly identical picture is one of the views of Morocco, showing similar geology.

NASA

Saudia Arabia

This kingdom is the largest country on the Arabian Peninsula, and site of the Islamic holy cities of Medina and Mecca. Its modern foundation dates from 1902 when Ibn Saud, a descendant of an eighteenth-century ruling family, began his reconquest of the country.

The shifting pattern of history brought Saudi Arabia into sudden international prominence in 1936 when oil was discovered in this desert land. Rapid development of the oil fields in recent years brought the country to the fourth rank in world production of petroleum.

In the search for likely drill sites, Saudi Arabia was "explored" by aerial photography. One result has been a detailed study of the country's geology, unusual for so arid a region. The Arabian Peninsula is a tilted plateau with the high edge of a mountainous escarpment of igneous or

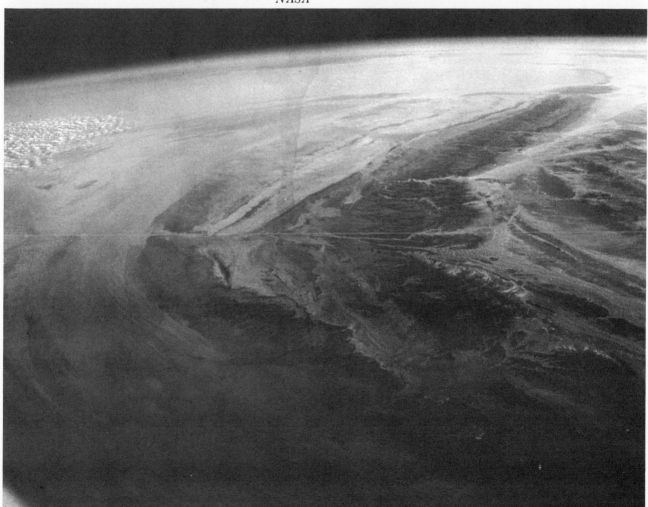

once-molten rock along the Red Sea shore. These mountains, along with ranges of sedimentary rock on the Gulf of Aden and in Muscat on the Gulf of Oman, block moist ocean air from the interior. In the previous section of this atlas aerial views of the Red Sea and Gulf of Oman show the coastline, while the text describes the widening Red Sea.

Aerial photography in desert regions is often striking in its detail because the surface is barren. Views of sand dunes are important geologically for comparison with ancient dune patterns "fossilized" in the sedimentary rocks, often underground in other regions of the world.

Major oil centers of the Arabian peninsula are on the shallow shore of the Persian Gulf. Rocks in the Suda Biyad area, north of Bahrein, are marine deposits. They were laid down at the same time as those of the Gulf Coast of the United States. Overall, a coating of windborne material blankets the rocks.

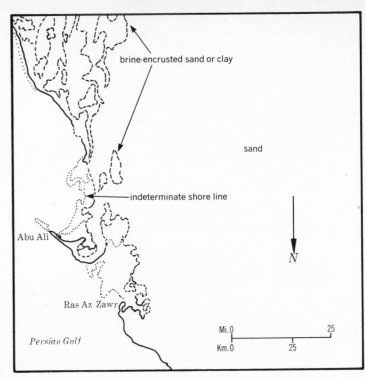

NASA

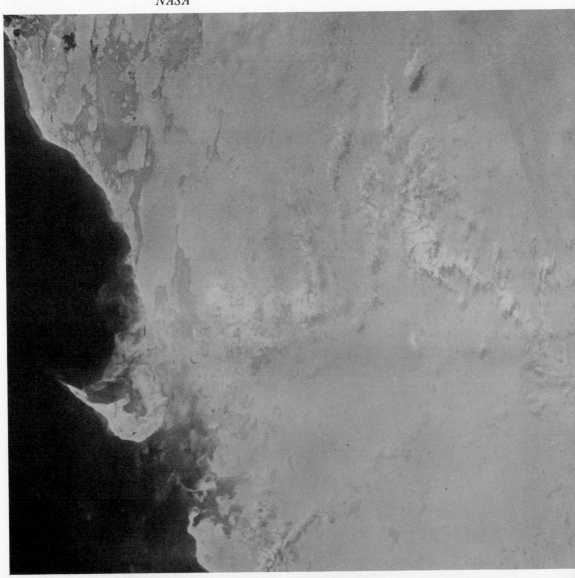

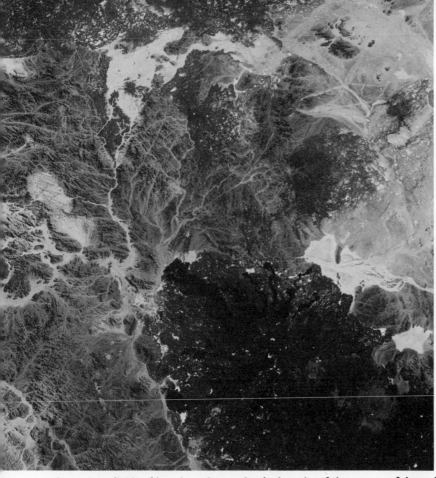

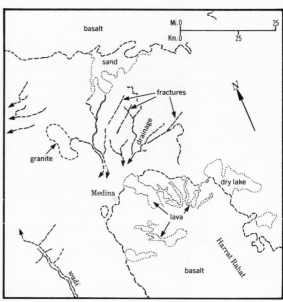

Great lava fields of basalt make up the dark rocks of the Hejaz section of Saudi Arabia. Medina, a holy city of Islam, lies on ancient rocks at the edge of the younger lava surrounded by lighter-toned surface deposits.

NASA

Rub' al Khali, the "Empty Quarter" desert of Saudi Arabia, is one of the largest single sand-dune regions in the world. Unlike the Sahara, it has few rock outcrops. Some of the dunes extend without a break for more than 100 miles (160.9 kilometers).

NASA

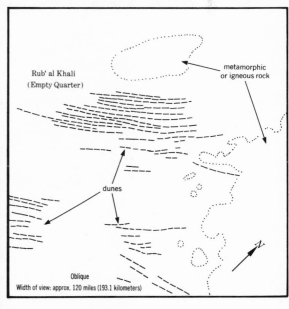

175

Kuwait

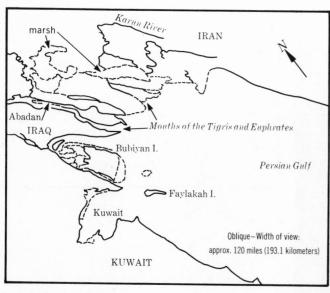

marsh
Karun River
IRAN
N
Abadan
IRAQ
Mouths of the Tigris and Euphrates
Bubiyan I.
Persian Gulf
Faylakah I.
Kuwait
Oblique—Width of view:
approx. 120 miles (193.1 kilometers)
KUWAIT

This small monarchy, about the size of Connecticut, is the world's second-largest exporter and fifth-largest producer of crude oil. Oil reserves in Kuwait, before the Prudhoe Bay, Alaska, discoveries, were estimated to be about one-quarter of the world total.

The aerial views of Kuwait City on these pages show the dramatic effect of the country's oil royalty income ($3,000 per capita annually) on what was a quiet pearl-fishing port and market town until 1938. In the central section of the city that most striking features are a number of large

Warehouses, office buildings, and paved roads contrast in Kuwait with the dusty streets of the residential sections. On the waterfront, local small craft, used for pearling and fishing, are visible inside the breakwater.

Fairey Surveys, Ltd.

This aerial view of a traditional Arab village on the outskirts of Kuwait city is typical, with its walled gardens and hand-dug wells. Modern buildings and telegraph poles indicate some of the material gains for Kuwait from oil royalties.

Fairey Surveys, Ltd.

buildings and the many wide boulevards. Strategically placed rotaries eliminate the need for traffic lights. Contrasting with this view is that of the older community with its narrow lanes, the only visible concession to modernity being power-line poles.

Wadi Hadhramaut cuts deep into flat-bedded deposits topped with dark shale in Southern Yemen. The country was a British protectorate until independence in 1967, when it merged with Aden, the South Arabian Federation, and several sheikdoms and sultanates on the Gulf of Aden. The Wadi is typical of the topography of the southern shore of the peninsula.   *NASA*

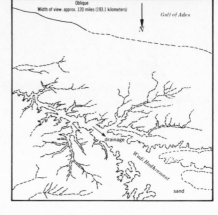

Ras al Hadd, the easternmost point of the Arabian peninsula, is a sandy foreland being built eastward by sediments from the Gulf of Oman. Trend lines along the Arabian Sea shore show deposits laid down on a shelf of older igneous, metamorphic and sedimentary rocks at the foot of the mountains.   *NASA*

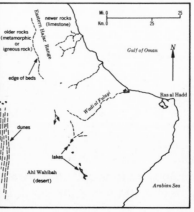

Muscat and Oman
Persian Gulf Federation
Southern South Yemen

Fringing Saudi Arabia to the east and south are a number of small sheikdoms and sultanates, originally founded as trading centers on the narrow coastal plains. The discovery of oil in these coastal regions, in the 1950's, is a dramatic new factor to the rulers and population of these tiny countries.

The accompanying photographs show three segments of the Arabian Peninsula coast and some nearly classic geologic features. In the view of the Wadi Hadhramaut, flat-lying sedimentary beds are apparent by the color contrast between the uppermost and those underlying.

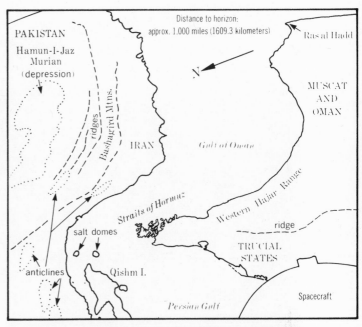

A region of geologic complexity lines the Straits of Hormuz, Persian Gulf, and Gulf of Oman, shown in this Gemini 12 photograph. The Ras al Hadd is visible in the picture, as are the sweeping Hajar mountains of Muscat and Oman. *NASA*

The lower Tigris River in Iraq and the nearby Zagros Mountains in Iran have been inhabited by man since Neanderthal times, about 75,000 years ago. The highly eroded ranges of the Zagros and Kabir ranges overlook saline lakes in the desert lowlands.

NASA

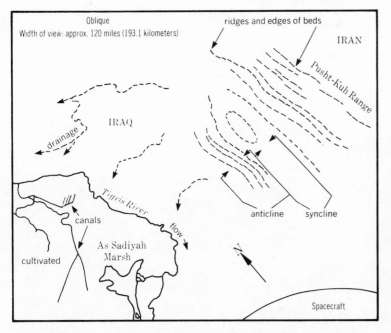

Iraq

Modern Iraq covers most of ancient Mesopotamia, a Greek name meaning "between rivers," and a reference to the Tigris and Euphrates. The present name was chosen in 1921, when Turkish rule ended and a British mandate began. In 1932 Iraq became an independent Arab state.

The vast alluvial plain watered by the Tigris and Euphrates and their tributaries is dotted with the sites of some of the world's first cities which grew from villages about five thousand years ago.

Mosul, in northern Iraq, lies on the west bank of the Tigris. An important city in ancient Mesopotamia, it gave its name to muslin cloth. Today it is an agricultural and petroleum center. Modern boulevards and parks contrast with the winding streets and alleys of the older sections in this aerial view.　　*Fairey Surveys, Ltd.*

Through the centuries, the city states of Nippur, Ur, and Babylon, and the nations of Assyria, whose capital was Nineveh, and Chaldea succeeded one another as rulers of the great arable plain of Mesopotamia. Finally, conquerors from Persia, Macedonia, and Rome reduced the area to colonial status. References to Mesopotamian kingdoms in biblical lore show the power and importance of these ancient dominions in shaping Judaism and Christianity.

Iraq is a veritable archaeological treasure house. The wheel, oxcart, packass, metallurgy, and the potter's wheel originated or saw early use

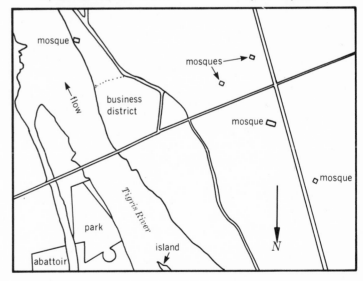

181

Nineveh, capital of the Assyrian Empire until its fall in 612 B.C., is visible largely because of its great perimeter wall. Covered with sown fields today, here and there the trenches of archaeological excavation are apparent. The sheer size of the project limits complete excavation.

Fairey Surveys, Ltd.

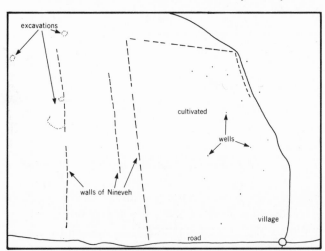

in what is now Iraq. Complex irrigation projects were used to water the fields until their destruction during the Moslem and later invasions. Excavation and discovery of decorative and useful objects in Iraq have shown that the urbanization of Mesopotamia has a relative parallel to the increased size of cities in our own time.

In developing the art of governing and operating a functioning urban society the ancient Mesopotamians established some of the key patterns of life today. Among their inventions are: a monetary system, the division of the day into twenty-four hours and the circle into 360 degrees, and a host of essential civil-engineering practices.

Iraq is one of the world's great oil producers, an important source of income for the development of irrigation projects along the Tigris and Euphrates.

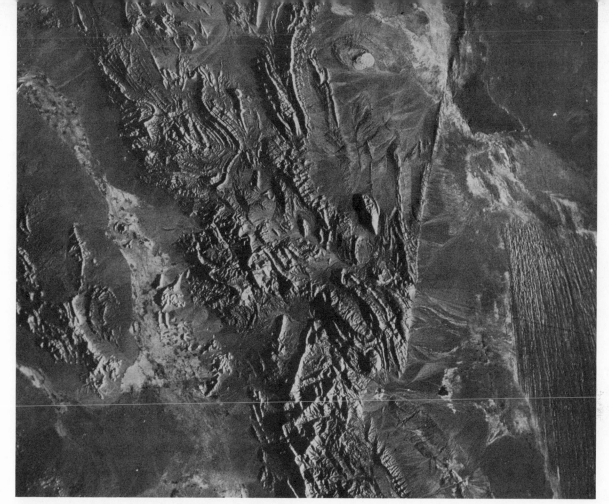

In central Iran the Zagros Mountains slope down to the great desert plateau. This section of the Dasht-I-Lut (which means "Firm Desert" in Persian) has a few fertile valleys lying between towering, barren peaks. Kerman city is an ancient goat's wool and carpet center. Lake Namakzas nearby is a marsh filling the lowest part of the Lut.

NASA

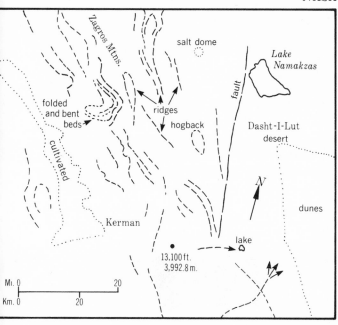

Iran

Often called Persia, after the Pars, an ancient people of the southern part of the country, Iran has an unusually long historical continuity. Iran means Aryan, the name of the people from the northwest who first settled the plateau south of the Caspian Sea.

The great figures of the Persian Empire, Darius, Cyrus the Great, Cyrus the Younger and the Ten Thousand, and Xerxes, made a powerful impact on the Eastern and Western worlds over twenty centuries ago. The capital of the Persian Empire, Persepolis, lies in ruins today but was in regal splendor from 559 to 331 B.C., when it was burned after Alexander the Great conquered Persia. Persepolis was begun by Darius as a political capital where he could meet and receive

Despite the ruggedness of the Zagros Mountains, their valleys have been settled for thousands of years. Persepolis, ceremonial capital of Darius I, Xerxes, and later kings of the Achaemenid Empire, lies in a valley near Niriz and Tasht salt lakes. Nearby, a neolithic village (not shown), dating from about 4000 B.C., is evidence of early habitation.

NASA

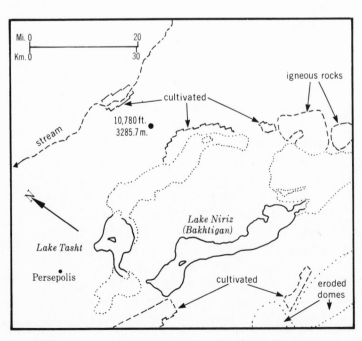

delegations from the various peoples of the Persian Empire in a kind of social atmosphere divorced from diplomatic and administrative forms. Later, Xerxes extended the dimensions of Persepolis, and furthered the policy of ritual homage to the Persian leaders.

Oil was discovered in Iran early in this century, and a pipeline to the refinery center of Abadan, at the head of the Persian Gulf, was completed in 1913. By 1950 Abadan was the world's largest refining center. Today jumbo tankers ply the gulf on their way to the Orient, particularly Japan, or Europe.

Geographically, Iran is an arid country, rimmed to the south by the Zagros Mountains and to the north by the Elburz. In between these ranges lies a great desert basin with smaller basins to the south enclosed by branching ranges.

A low-attitude view of the excavated palace at Persepolis shows its ornate plan. The buildings were burned during a visit by Alexander the Great in A.D. 324, and lay virtually forgotten until first described in modern times during the seventeenth century. The chains of holes visible in the photograph are ventilation and access shafts of qanat aqueducts.

Courtesy of the Oriental Institute, University of Chicago

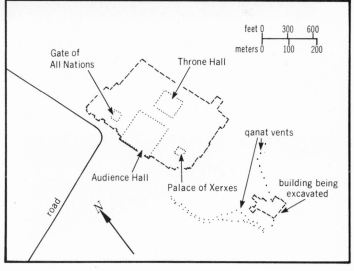

Most of the population is settled in the northwest Highlands of the Zagros Mountains where rainfall is greater.

Despite the arid climate over much of Iran, the country not only manages to feed its own people, but also produces crops for export. Irrigation of agricultural areas is aided by a three-thousand-year-old method of underground aqueducts called *qanats*. Seventy-five percent of all the water used in the country is supplied by more than 170,000 miles (273,588.5 kilometers) of hand-dug qanats. The first qanats were used by farmers who domesticated cereal grain and began man's move away from a strictly nomadic existence.

185

Afghanistan

Modern Afghanistan dates from the mid-1920's with an emphasis on neutrality and development of the land. The high mountain chains of the central part of the country stretch above fertile valleys and combine in the towering Hindu Kush on the Pakistan-India border. The lowest pass in central Afghanistan is over 9,000 feet (2,743.2 meters) high. In the Hindu Kush (Hindu Killer),

a range second only to the Himalayas in height, elevations reach more than 24,000 feet (7,315.2 meters).

Runoff from the mountains provides water for irrigation and new hydroelectric power plants in this generally arid country. Almost half of the country's foreign exchange comes from the sale of karakul, or Persian lamb skins. Cotton has been exported since 1870, but the green fields are small compared to some of the southern deserts, among the most desolate in the world.

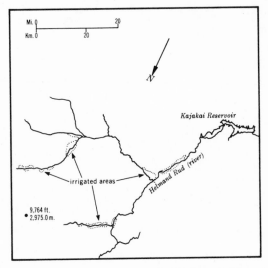

In this oblique view of north-central Afghanistan, looking into the U.S.S.R., barren mountains rise high above fertile valleys. For centuries this part of Asia was crossed by caravans on the silk route from China to the west. Much of the area in this Gemini 5 photograph is the fabled Turkestan, site of Samarkand, Tashkent, the Amu Darya (Oxus) River, and Bactria, home of the double-humped camel. *NASA*

The Kajakai Reservoir on the Helmand River is one of several large man-made lakes in Afghanistan used to hold water that would otherwise drain into the sands of the Seistan Desert. The Helmand is one of the longest rivers entirely inside the country, and, with its tributaries, has the potential of adding 44 percent to the arable land area. *NASA*

Union of Soviet Socialist Republics

The formation of the U.S.S.R. in 1922 created what is still the world's largest country. Virtually every climate and natural resource is found in some part of the Soviet Union, which covers northern Asia and part of eastern Europe. The shores of the Black Sea are a popular summer resort area. In Siberia, new cities, industry, and hydroelectric projects show the energetic exploitation of virgin lands despite the extremely cold winters.

With the United States, the Soviet Union dominates space flight. Many Soviet satellites of the Cosmos series are designed to provide meteorological data in connection with the World Weather Watch. Although the Soviets are taciturn about public release of data from their space exploration, it seems likely that some satellites are, or will be, used to photograph the natural resources of the vast, unsettled regions. Also

This night-time Nimbus 1 photograph of the earth shows a Pole-to-Pole strip across the U.S.S.R., the Arabian Peninsula, and Africa. The use of infrared photography by satellites permits a twenty-four-hour watch on the world's weather. *NASA*

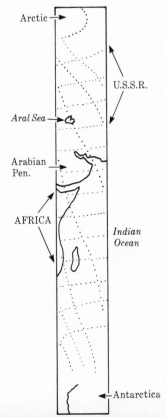

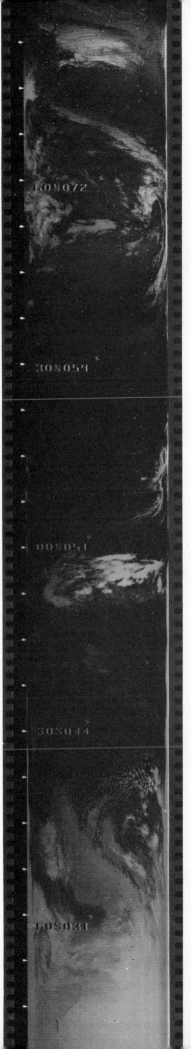

satellite and aircraft-borne remote sensors are being applied to agriculture, water supply, timber analysis, geology, and other resources of inaccessible regions.

Structurally, the U.S.S.R. is composed of the Russian and Siberian Platforms — part of the ancient supercontinent Laurasia. Several mountain ranges of sedimentary material were folded on the edges of the solid platform. Central and eastern Siberia is a plateau separated from mountains to the east by a once-volcanic region of igneous rocks studded with fluelike, diamond-bearing pipes. The Caspian and Aral Seas are saline remnants apparently of old incursions of the ocean into the Laurasia landmass.

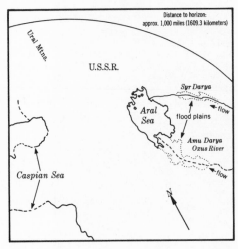

Both the Caspian and Aral Seas are saline lakes. The Caspian is the world's largest lake, and drains the Volga River. Like the Caspian, the Aral Sea fills the bottom of a great basin, its principal source of water being the Amu Darya (Oxus), flowing from the Pamir Mountains.
NASA

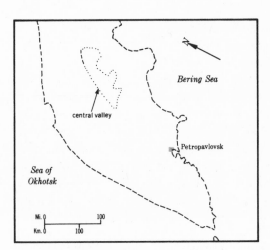

The Kamchatka peninsula encloses the Sea of Okhotsk on the Pacific shore of the U.S.S.R. Rugged and volcanic, the peninsula is part of the circum-Pacific "Ring of Fire." Bezymianny, a volcano on Kamchatka, virtually blew up in 1956, spewing dust to a height of nearly 28 miles (about 45 kilometers).
NASA

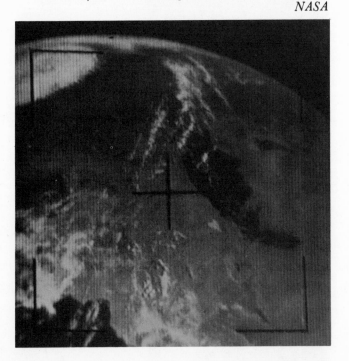

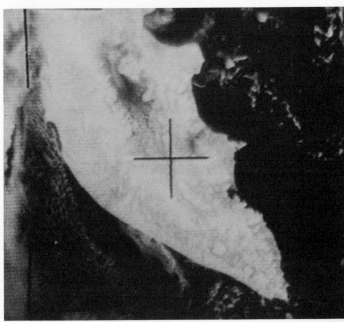

Most of the Indian subcontinent is visible in this Gemini 11 photograph, taken with a wide-angle lens from an altitude of 460 miles (740.2 kilometers). As the home of some of the world's oldest civilizations, the great peninsula was a fabled land in Europe, and interest in it led directly to the discovery of the New World.   *NASA*

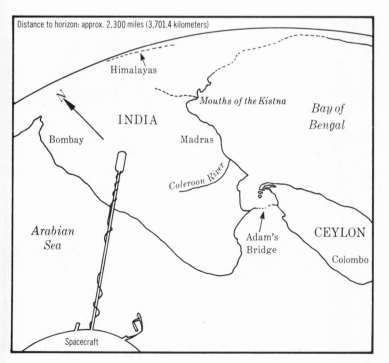

Ceylon Pakistan India

The countries of the Indian subcontinent were created after World War II from the India governed by the British since 1774. India, the largest, is an ancient land whose language and religion are predominantly Hindu, but where fifteen official languages and 850 others, including dialects, show a cultural and linguistic diversity. Pakistan is an Urdu-speaking Moslem state divided into two sections 1,000 miles (1,609.3 kilometers) apart on opposite sides of India. Ceylon is an island nation, somewhat larger than West Virginia, settled by Singhalese from the Ganges River valley about 540 B.C.

As part of Gondwanaland (named for a section

189

About half of the 130-degree bend of the Pamir and Hindu Kush ranges is visible in this view of the great mountainous plateau of Asia. The Khyber Pass, at lower right, is an ancient trade route between Afghanistan and Pakistan. At the top is the Takla Makan, a desert basin in western China.   *NASA*

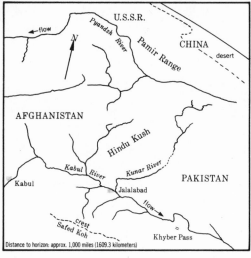

Southwest of the Pakistani capital of Islamabad lies the Salt Range, a folded and faulted region of marine deposits whose earliest rocks were laid down over 410 million years ago. Petroleum from the Dhulian field is piped to Rawalpindi, one of West Pakistan's major cities and former interim capital.   *NASA*

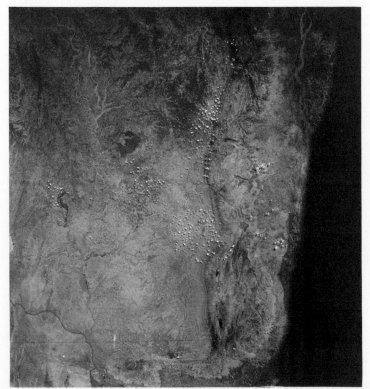

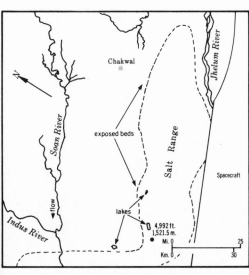

of India), the great crustal block of the subcontinent drifted across the equator about 3,107 miles (5,000 kilometers) with an anticlockwise rotation of 25 to 30 degrees. Part of crustal India slid under the continental mass of Laurasia, created a double-thick crust beneath Tibet. One result of this movement was the creation of the great Himalaya Range by warping of the surface plus uplift. The front of the Himalayas drops nearly vertically to river plains at the mountains' base.

The Himalayas are the easternmost part of a mountain belt that begins with the High Atlas of Morocco. In terms of the worldwide pattern of mountain building, called "orogeny" by geologists, the east-west Indo-Pakistani ranges met the north-south Nu and Yun Ling Shan of China to form the highlands of southeast Asia. Geologically, these latter are connected to the mountains of Indonesia.

The shallow Gulf of Kutch is bordered on the north by the Rann of Kutch, a marsh gradually filling the Gulf. The Rann is a completely desolate region, and, with the Gulf, fills the western end of a trough which begins at the foot of the Himalayas. *NASA*

The challenge of the Himalayas led to successive expeditions on lower peaks and final conquest of Mount Everest (29,028 feet, 8,847.8 meters) in 1953. Something of the scale of these great ranges can be seen in western Kashmir where the peak of Nanga Parbat (26,620 feet, 8,113 meters) lies only 25 air miles (40.2 kilometers) from the 3,000-foot (914.4 meter) elevation of the Indus River.

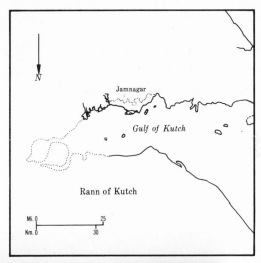

Coal, iron, gold, steel, asbestos, manganese, and a host of other minerals are found in the metamorphic, folded hills of India, creating an important industrial potential. Also, the deep gorges of swift-flowing rivers provide a source of hydroelectric power. Offshore, rich fishing grounds are exploited.

Most of West Pakistan is an alluvial plain with little rainfall where large-scale irrigation, begun by the British, provides not only an income from crops but sole means of survival for the people. East Pakistan, in strong contrast, is a rice-growing, very heavily populated, Bengali-oriented region.

Ceylon lies in the monsoon belt, and its wet lowlands were the first settled. The higher, dense rain forest has gradually succumbed to modern engineering as roads and railroads penetrate the interior of the island. Tea and rubber have long been principal Ceylonese products, followed by gemstones, spices, and graphite.

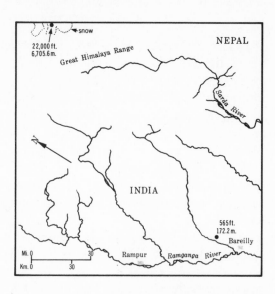

The great wall of the Himalaya front is evident in this view of the India-Nepal border. A short distance from the fertile Ganges River plain, snow-capped peaks jut skyward to form the southern edge of the Tibetan plateau.

NASA

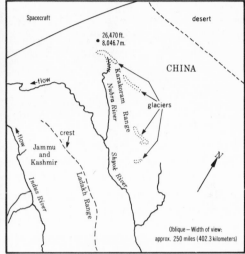

The Karakoram Range is separated from the Great Himalaya Range by the Indus River valley. Rapid uplift of the mountains, plus melting of the perpetual snow, helped the river cut its gorge more quickly. This section of the Himalaya system lies in Kashmir, a region claimed by both Pakistan and India. *NASA*

Mount Everest, the world's highest peak, on the Nepal-Tibet border, lies at the edge of the Himalayas. The Matsang (also known as Brahmaputra and Tsangpo) River runs the length of the Great Himalayas, and turns nearly 360 degrees to join the Ganges in East Pakistan. In this photograph the lake-filled basins of the southern Tibet section of China are visible. *NASA*

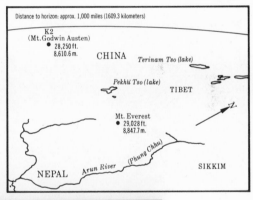

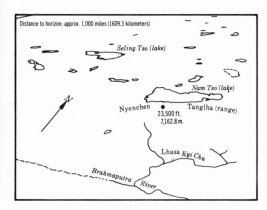

Seling Tso (lake)

Nam Tso (lake)

Nyenchen   *Tanglha (range)*
23,500 ft.
7,162.8 m.

Lhasa *Kyi Chu*

Brahmaputra River

Central Tibet, an autonomous section of China, is the world's highest plateau. The average elevation is 16,000 feet (4,876.8 meters). The area shown in the photograph once lay beneath the now vanished Tethys Sea between Laurasia and Gondwanaland about 130 million years ago.   *NASA*

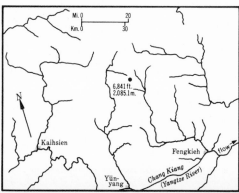

Mi. 0   20
Km. 0   30

6,841 ft.
2,085.1 m.

N

Kaihsien

Fengkieh   flow

Yün-yang   *Chang Kiang (Yangtze River)*

The Yangtze or Chang Kiang (River) is a vital communication and commerce route in China. It cuts its way from the Tibetan plateau to the sea near Shanghai. This view of the folded ranges of the Central Mountain Bloc shows why ground transport is difficult in this part of China.   *NASA*

China

Continuous use of the land in China* for ten thousand years has had an important effect on the country's geography. Many of the once tree-covered slopes have been highly eroded, with an attendant loss of soil. Carried downstream by several large rivers, enormous deltas have been built seaward. Cities and agricultural lands on the deltas have grown with the creation of new land from river-borne silt. This pattern was unintentional; nonetheless, the result shows the effect of man on his surroundings. Another geographical aspect of Chinese civilization is that the transportation system was almost entirely

*In this atlas the geographical name China refers to the People's Republic of China, sometimes called Mainland China or Red China. The Republic of China, sometimes known as Nationalist China, is also called Taiwan, after the large island on which it has its provisional capital.

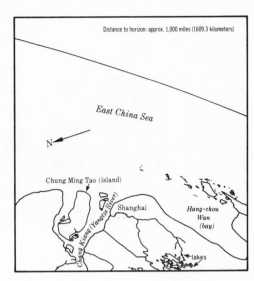

Distance to horizon: approx. 1,000 miles (1609.3 kilometers)

East China Sea

N

Chung Ming Tao (island)

Chung Kiang (Yangtze River)

Shanghai

Hang-chou Wan (bay)

lakes

Near Shanghai the Yangtze flows into the Yellow Sea, carrying silt and extending the shifting pattern of the delta. Satellite photographs, such as this by Gemini 5 astronauts, show the value of space photography for mapping, river studies, and land use. Shanghai is an industrial and intellectual center that grew owing to extraterritorial status granted to foreign governments.

NASA

195

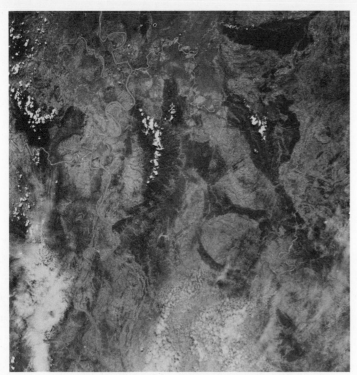

Silt-laden meandering rivers and barren hillsides characterize central Hunan Province, showing man's effect on the land. This section, around the city of Hengyang, has long been deforested and extensively cultivated, leaving little ground cover to retain and enrich the soil. Tin, antimony, and other minerals are mined in these hills.

NASA

South of Hang-chou Wan (Bay) below Shanghai, the China coastline changes from a smooth, flat topography to one of irregular, rocky promontories and numerous islands. Foochow, the Fugiu of Marco Polo, dates from the seventh century. Offshore the Ma-tsu Lieh-tao (Matsu and Pei-kan, or Changshu Islands) are heavily fortified Nationalist strongholds.

NASA

water-based until a few years ago. The first railway bridge ever built across the Yangtze Kiang (River) opened in 1957.

The geomorphology of China is complex, with extremes ranging from the Tibetan plateau and projecting peaks to the large plains of alluvium formed by the Hwang Yo (Yellow), Liao Ho, and Yangtze Kiang rivers. A number of folded ranges, mostly with elevations under 5,000 feet (1,524.0 meters), and with no dominant trend of direction, cover the southern and western parts of

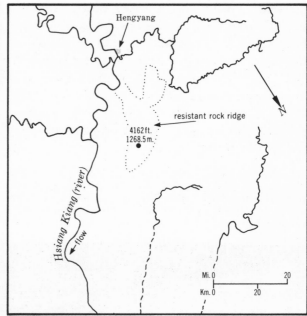

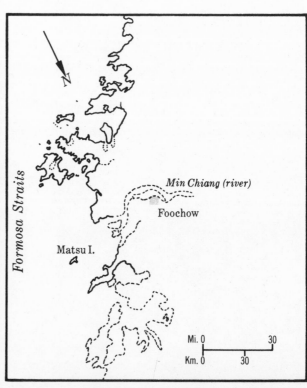

the country. From Manchuria south to Southeast Asia a discontinuous group of ranges borders on the Gobi and Ordos deserts and the Red Basin surrounding Chungking. North of the Tibetan Plateau the Tarim Basin of Sinkiang Province is a huge interior depression.

The Tibetan Plateau is a particularly impressive example of the forces that shape the earth's crust. Under the surface lies a double thickness of the earth's crust formed when continental drift carried peninsular India toward Asia and forced the Indian crustal segment under what was then a plain. Isostasy — the principle of crustal equilibrium — is demonstrated in Tibet by the geologically rapid uplift to an average height of 16,000 feet (4,876.8 meters) in about 80 million years. Marine sediments prove that the southern edge of the plateau was under the Tethys Sea only 135 million years ago.

China's chief pearl-fishing grounds are shown in this aerial view of the Kwangtung Province coast and the Gulf of Tonkin. Counterclockwise circulation of local currents is evident in the buildup of spits on the Lei-chou Pan-tao (Peninsula). Resistant rock ridges have forced the stream at the top of the photograph to be diverted from the shortest route to the sea.

NASA

This view of part of the deltaic plain of the Chu Kiang, or Pearl River, shows the pattern of sediments being borne into the South China Sea (Nan Hai). The 110-mile (177.02-kilometer) Chu Kiang is formed by the conflux of the Si, Peh, and Tung Kiang (rivers) near Kwangchow (Canton). On the coast the British colony of Hong Kong and the Portuguese enclave of Macao are the only European settlements remaining in China.

NASA

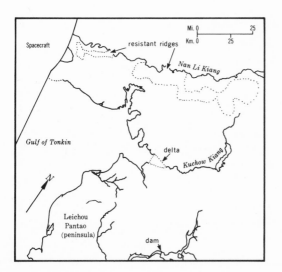

197

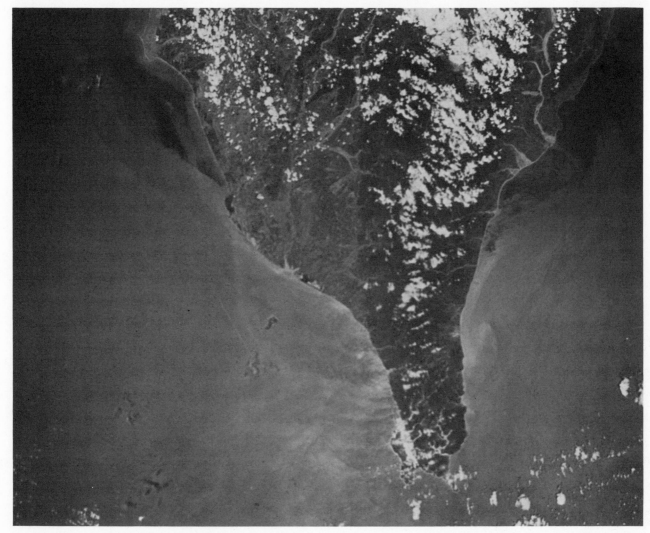

In this Gemini 10 photograph the forested, mountainous rib and wet coastal plain of semitropical Taiwan stand out sharply from the sunlit wave pattern of the sea. Mountains on the island rise to 13,113 feet (3,995.7 meters) with 48 peaks over 10,000 feet (3,048 meters) high.

NASA

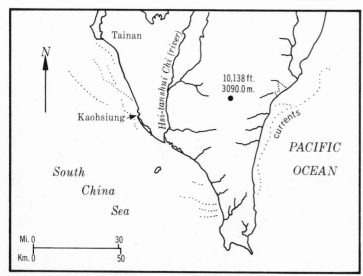

Republic of China

Territorially, the Republic of China, also known as Nationalist China, occupies the large island of Taiwan (Formosa) and a number of smaller islands of the Penghu group. Taipei, the chief city of Taiwan, has been the provisional capital of the Republic since 1949.

Taiwan is part of the western Pacific chain of volcanic islands that extends from Alaska and Japan through Indonesia. The heavily forested mountain spine of eastern Taiwan drops precipitously into the Pacific, with a narrow gorge paralleling the coast, the only inhabited section. Along the western shore an alluvial plain at the foot of the mountains faces the Formosa Strait. Most of the agricultural section lies on the northern, wider, part of this plain, but the southern plain and lower hillsides are agricultural.

Deep embayments, such as those of the Honshu coast, offer sheltered harbors and local fishing grounds in southern Japan. Osaka, hub of the Kinki or Han-shin, the Japanese industrial complex, is the country's second largest city. Nagoya, an administrative center since the second century, is modern Japan's chief textile center.

NASA

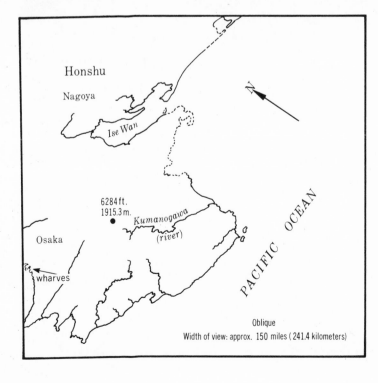

Honshu

Nagoya

Ise Wan

6284 ft.
1915.3 m.

Kumanogawa
(river)

Osaka

wharves

PACIFIC OCEAN

Oblique
Width of view: approx. 150 miles (241.4 kilometers)

Japan

With the highest population density of any country in the world, Japanese agriculture uses highly developed forms of such Asian practices as double- and inter-cropping (two crops planted simultaneously in one field), terraced fields, elaborate systems of irrigation, and high fertilization. Some of this attitude has been utilized in sea farming, where pearl oysters, fish, seaweed, and other fresh- and salt-water products are agriculturally produced.

Japan's four main islands, Hokkaido, Honshu,

199

Shikoku, and Kyushu, form most of an island arc, a geologically connected range of volcanic mountains. Many geologists believe that island arcs, and their accompanying seaward underwater trench, prove that the sea floor is spreading outward from midocean ridges to dip under the continental mass.

Actually, Japan is part of five different arcs that joined about 25 million years ago when the islands moved outward from Asia as separate segments of land.

Subtropical Kyushu is fringed on the Suwo Nada with wet-rice fields, while the interior is mixed forest and agriculture. The island is the southermost of the main islands, and supplies half of Japan's coal. Its few ports and small villages offer a centuries-old semirural contrast to the megalopolis centers on Honshu.

NASA

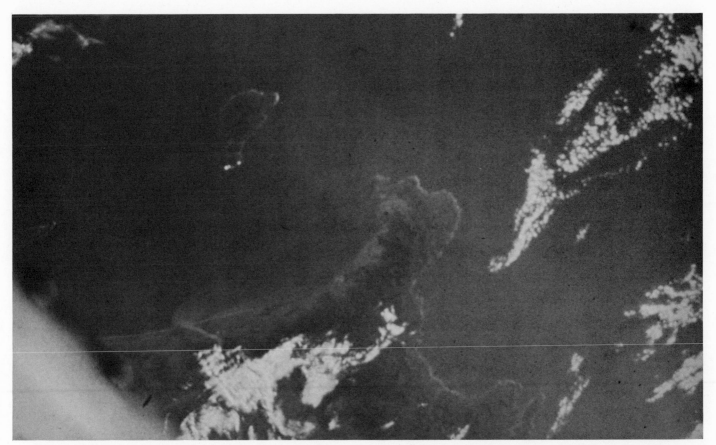

Cape Engaño, at the northern tip of Luzon Island, lies at the end of the Sierra Madre, a range that forms the steep Pacific flank of the island. The Cagayan River is the principal navigable waterway of the Philippines tobacco growing region. In this Gemini 5 photograph, river-borne sediments are visible as they are swept seaward by swift currents in the Babuyan Channel.

NASA

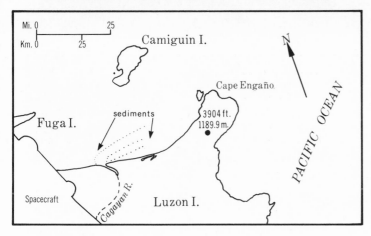

Philippines

Like Japan, the Philippine Islands are the volcanic mountain peaks of an island arc jutting up from a very deep seaward trench. This combination is one of the essential elements in geologic study of the Pacific Ocean basin with applications to continental drift and the newly developed theory of sea-floor spreading.

The Philippine, or Mindanao, Trench has a maximum depth of 34,446 feet (10,499 meters). As previously noted, many geologists theorize that the trenches represent a region of movement where the ocean floor is forcing its way down and under the continental mass represented by the islands. Most of the Pacific Ocean trenches lie

201

The rugged spine of southern Luzon is traced by clouds over the mountain peaks. Mount Mayon (7,943 feet, 2,421 meters) is an active volcano, often described as the world's most perfect cone. The lowlands of this part of Luzon are the abaca-growing center of the Philippines.
NASA

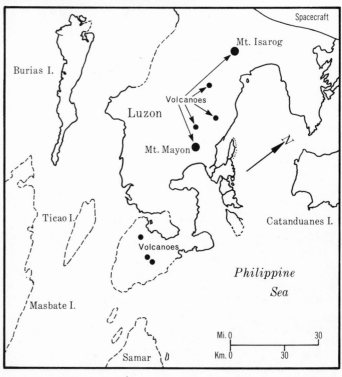

close to the continent (on the east) or along island arcs just off the continental block.

A clue to the geophysical picture of the crust are the volcanoes of island arcs. Taal and Mayon are the most active volcanoes in the islands, and nearly a dozen eruptions in recent times have been recorded.

Vulcanism provides the Philippines necessary soil for their agriculturally based economy. The islands' most famous product is Manila, or abaca, hemp made from the coarser fibers of a strain of banana plant native to the islands. Used Manila hemp is converted to Manila paper.

202

Burma

From the mountainous north the country's dominant geographical force, the Irrawaddy (Elephant) River flows to fan out into a 150-mile-wide (241.4 kilometers) delta. The delta is 180 miles (289.6 kilometers), and lies 1,400 miles (2,253 kilometers) from the Irrawaddy's headwaters. Two-thirds of the river's length is navigable.

Lower Burma, a wet-rice zone and site of the capital city, Rangoon, is partly separated from Upper Burma (whose chief city is Mandalay) by a dry zone, a semiarid region. East of the dry zone the upland Shan Plateau is a forest and grassland series of ranges extending to the border with Laos.

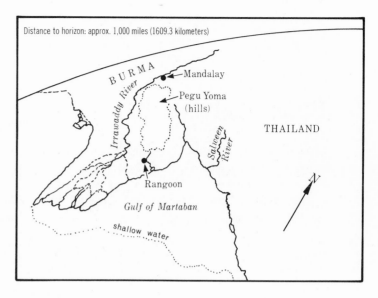

In this Gemini 10 view of the mouths of the Irrawaddy and the Tenasserim section of the Burma coast, the rain-forest-covered granite hills and wet-rice zone of the delta are visible. Teak from the forest, which has the world's great annual rainfall, and rice, planted in water-covered paddies, are Burma's chief agricultural exports.

NASA

Thailand

The geology of Thailand, like that of neighboring Burma, is the result of the great orogenic sequence that was part of the closing of the Tethys Sea between Gondwanaland and Laurasia. The aptly named "Tin Ranges" of Malaysia and Thailand were formed between 180 and 140 million years ago. Thailand is the world's third-largest producer of tin ore, but well behind the leading source, Malaysia.

Rice production, by irrigation from the main river the Chao Phraya and its tributaries, is the mainstay of the Thai economy. Teak and other hardwoods are cut from the nearly 70 percent of the country that is forested and floated to market. Elephants provide the power for logging operations.

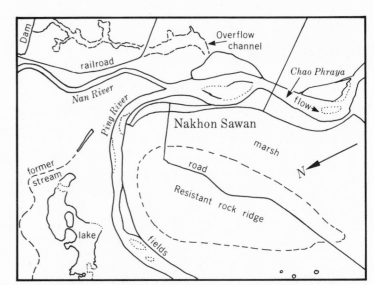

Nakhon Sawan, an important commercial center in the central valley of Thailand, lies on the Chao Phraya, where this river is formed by the confluence of the Ping and Yom rivers. In this aerial photograph, the linearity, typical of many Thai riverbank towns, is apparent. The single river bridge is indicative of the dependence on waterways for transport.

Fairey Surveys, Ltd.

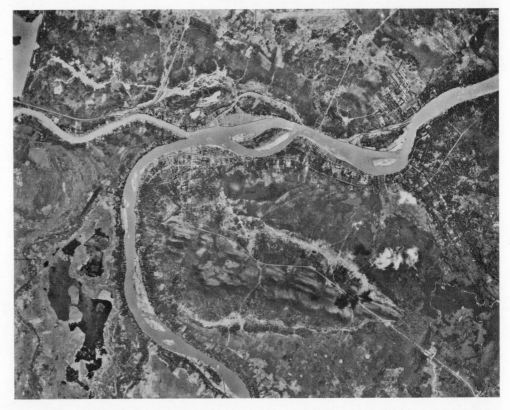

Southeast Asia

The small nations of Southeast Asia (see key map) offer striking differences in culture, economy, and other geographical factors based almost entirely on altitude. Mountains and plateaus are forested, with lumbering and mining (especially in Malaysia) the chief industries. On the broad alluvial plains rice — the most important crop — as well as cotton, yams, sugar cane, and tobacco, is grown. Malaysia also specializes in rubber, coconuts, and pineapples.

The north-south ranges of hills are extensions of the complex cordillera of Burma, Thailand, and China. Geologically they can be traced into Indonesia. During periods of lowered sea level, when much of the world's water was locked in the great ice sheets, the southern part of the South China Sea was dry land. Drowned river valleys can be traced well out into the present ocean.

All of Southeast Asia is covered in this single Nimbus 2 photograph made from an altitude of 700 miles (1,126.5 kilometers). The clarity with which mountain trends and weather patterns appear in satellite photographs is a particularly useful aspect of the space program. The Mekong, Salween, and Irrawaddy rivers have their headwaters in the highlands of southern China.

ESSA

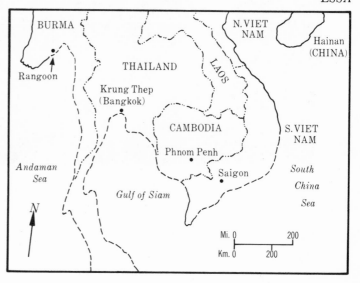

Most of the Pacific Ocean and Australia are visible in this ATS 2 satellite photograph taken from an altitude of 6,500 miles (10,460 kilometers). Australia is about the size of the continental United States, and offers a size comparison to the dimensions of the Pacific. About two-thirds of the Pacific is shown in the photograph.

NASA

Part VII
AUSTRALIA OCEANIA

The vast Pacific Basin, more than three times the size of Eurasia, the world's largest landmass, has increasingly become an object of scientific interest. Only during the past two decades has it become possible to traverse the region quickly by aircraft or to probe the depths accurately by sensitive depth sounders. The rift valley of the East Pacific Rise, the deep trenchs off the island arcs, the development of the many coral atolls are broad features of recent study.

Australia, the world's smallest continent, lies between the Indian Ocean and the Coral and Tasman Seas segments of the Pacific. Most of the country is low-lying desert or tropical or steppe in vegetation, with few population centers. Its distance from major markets in Europe, before the jet age, had a damping effect on immigration despite the vast areas of land available for settlement.

Oceania is an omnibus term used for the chains of coral atolls and volcanic islands scattered across most of the western Pacific. Major subdivisions are Polynesia to the north and east, Micronesia to the west, and Melanesia to the south.

Hawaii, the northeasternmost part of Polynesia, is one of the United States comprising most of the Hawaiian Islands, a lengthy volcanic chain.

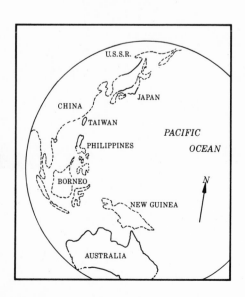

Eighty Mile Beach on the coast of western Australia is a name indicative of the impression made on early English explorers. Many French geographical names on the western coast date from a single survey made by the *Naturaliste* early in the nineteenth century. Those of much of the rest of the coast were assigned by Matthew Flinders, whose ship was the first to circumnavigate Australia. Flinders was so modest he named nothing after himself, but his name was often used by later geographers as a tribute.

NASA

Australia

Unlike every other large landmass except Antarctica, Australia had little prehistoric settlement and no extensive indigenous culture. This isolation, despite its relative nearness to Asia and the sailing abilities of Oriental and Oceania seamen is a cultural curiosity. Anthropologists feel that the first men to reach Australia settled there at least 25,000 years ago, judging by stone implements and cave paintings that have been dated by radiocarbon techniques. These early arrivals were apparently akin to the modern aborigines whose Stone Age culture is one of the few glimpses modern man has into his own past.

Australia's physical isolation from any other landmass also led to distinctive forms of plant and animal life. The eucalyptus tree, an often gigantic variety of myrtle, is a well-known example of Australian flora. Animals and birds such as the koala bear, kangaroo and wallaby, platypus, emu, and black swan are distinctive natives of the southern continent.

As a landmass Australia was once part of Gondwanaland. Although many geologists align the southern Great Australian Bight with the Antarctica coast of Wilkes Land before continental drift, there is disagreement as to whether Australia or Antarctica lay parallel to the eastern coast of the Indian peninsula. Part of the problem stems from unraveling the distorted sequence of rocks.

The oldest rocks in Australia are those of a sediment-filled trough running south from the Gulf of Carpentaria to the Flinders Range and the Spencer Gulf near Adelaide. These sediments were washed off the slopes of even older long-vanished mountains, more than 500 million years ago. Even more important to geologists is that the sediments are glacial deposits, indicative of an Ice Age present in both Northern and Southern hemispheres, distinctive from those of the Pleistocene epoch. (The oldest evidence of extensive glaciation is a group of deposits in Michigan that has been dated to over 2,500 million years ago).

Australia was again glaciated about 260 million years ago, at the same time that North America had a mild climate whose plants later became the extensive coal beds of the Appalachians. As the ice in Australia receded, the climate warmed to allow the growth of carboniferous plants between 235 and 200 million years ago. During the most recent advance of continental glaciers, which ended about 15,000 years ago, Australia was ice free except for the highest elevation.

The geography of Australia today is of an arid land with a humid belt along the eastern and northern coasts. The eastern side of the continent is mountainous in temperature latitudes, and traps onshore winds off the Tasman Sea. Behind the eastern highlands lie several large basins whose porous sedimentary rocks hold subsurface water within reach of drilled wells. This water is the key to life support on the great stations (ranches) of Australia. The western three-fifths of the nation is mostly covered by the arid Western Plateau. In additional several large sand deserts detract from the open lands available for settlement in Australia.

Mount Kosciusko is Australia's highest peak, with an elevation of 7,328 feet (2,233 meters). Because this relatively low elevation on a landmass the size of the continental United States

Oblique—Width of view: approx. 2,000 miles (3,218.6 kilometers)

Broome

Eighty Mile Beach

Western Australia

Lake Mackay

Timor Sea

Darwin

Northern Territory

Cape Arnhem

Gulf of Carpentaria

Spacecraft

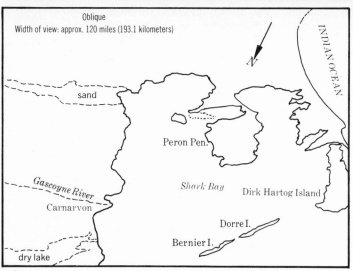

The shallow waters of Shark Bay, with feature names such as Disappointment Reach and Hopeless Reach, illustrate the lack of good natural harbors in Australia. Near Carnarvon a NASA tracking station is used for space studies and also for communications during Mercury, Gemini, and now Apollo flights. Inland, a vast desert shows few signs of human habitation.

NASA

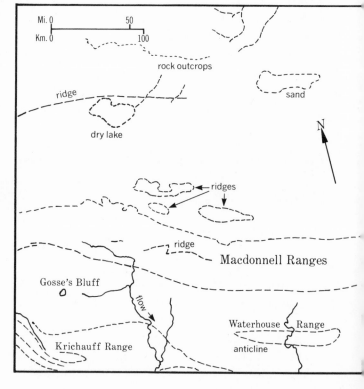

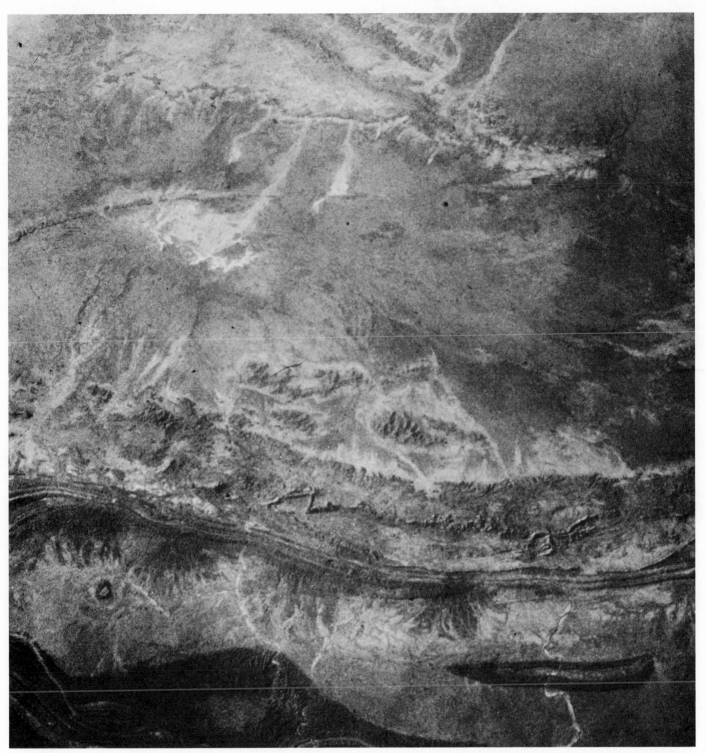

affects the average height above sea level, Australia has the lowest average elevation of any continent.

Although the first European settlement in Australia was a penal colony near present Sydney, the history of the Commonwealth more properly began with the early nineteenth-century era of colonization. In 1851 a gold rush in Victoria and New South Wales gave impetus to

This photograph of central Australia near Alice Springs was used by geologists as a clue to the comet impact origin of Gosse's Bluff, visible in the lower left. This 12-mile wide (19.3 kilometers), shallow crater was later examined on the ground, and recorded as the second known site where a comet struck the earth. The first site is at Tunguska, Siberia.

NASA

211

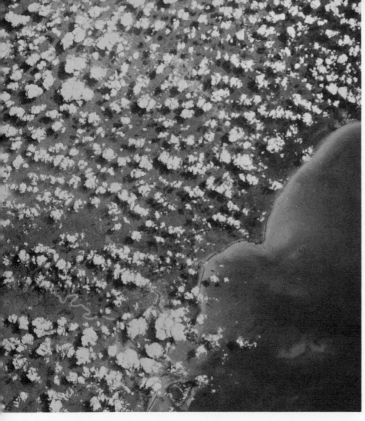

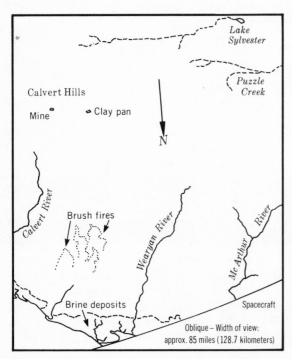

Along the northern, tropical coast of Australia, mangrove swamps fringe the shallow waters. This Gemini 5 photograph of the South Alligator River, east of Darwin, shows the inhospitable nature of the region. Over the land are small cumulus clouds, typical of the tropics.

NASA

Short, shallow rivers, internal drainage, and little rain distinguish a pastoral inland belt nearly encircling Australia. The southern shore of the Gulf of Carpentaria is typical of this pastoral belt. Inland, the Barkly Tableland forms a watershed. The Calvert Hills are the site of some lead and zinc mining operations.

NASA

the settlement of the temperate southeastern coast. The vast grasslands were quickly converted to pasture for sheep and cattle or plowed to grow wheat. Both commodities have been an export staple of the economy since the mid-nineteenth century, and Australia is one of the world's leading producers of both.

In 1965 vast iron deposits were discovered in western Australia, creating a boom in a particularly remote section. The largest known coal reserves in the Southern Hemisphere are on the coast around Sydney. Recently, new petroleum deposits have been found with a major field offshore in the Indian Ocean on the central Western Australia coast. Important uranium deposits are mined in northwestern Queensland. The value, in Australian dollars, of mineral production has passed that of wheat and wool since 1965, despite a generally favorable price for Australian produce.

Exploitation of Australia's natural resources at a rapid pace has created problems at the same time that new discoveries are being made. The Great Barrier Reef, the 1,200-mile (1,931.2-kilometer) coral chain off northern Queensland was suggested as a source of limestone to reduce the acidity of sugarcane fields. Opposition by biologists led to refusal of a mining lease but to the discovery that the live coral was being destroyed by an invasion of predatory starfish.

In the "outback" many areas have been overgrazed, and dust storms have increased. Australian agronomists are hopeful new range practices will be enforced before a perpetual desert is formed. The discovery of huge underground reservoirs of good water by oil prospectors near Alice Springs promises the possibility of irrigation for part of the desolate Western Plateau.

With few deepwater ports, Australia has a perennial transport problem. Early in 1969 the Government requested the United States to supply atomic explosives to blast a harbor site on the coast of Western Australia at Cape Keraudren. Vessels using the harbor could then avoid the long voyage to the south. Another attempt to shorten sea passage to Australia is a projected dredging of the shallow Torres Strait between the Cape York peninsula and the Papua half of New Guinea.

Australia's northernmost extension, the Cape York peninsula, has a mountainous eastern edge geologically connected to Papua on New Guinea island across the shallow Torres Strait. Offshore, to the east, lies the Great Barrier Reef, largest coral reef in the world.

NASA

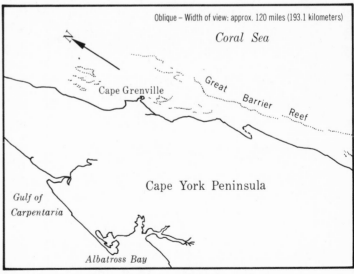

213

Oceania

The island and atoll reefs of the Pacific Ocean have grown on or above or around volcanic islands. The reefs themselves are formed of colonies of thousands of live coral polyps growing in a small cup-shaped framework of calcareous material. They require warm, clear, shallow salt water to survive. Long-term sea-level fluctuations and temperature changes kill the coral, but a reversal of the trend can revive a reef. Most live reefs today are not older than 20,000 years.

Ancient reefs, formed of coral or limestone, are often found buried far from the present shore. They are an excellent guide to the climate and location of long-vanished seas. Material from these extinct reefs is quarried for building stone and cement.

Like most coral atolls of the Pacific, the Tuamotu Archipelago is strung out in a southeast-to-northwest line. Polynesian settlements on the islands are supported by local fishing, copra harvests, and pearl diving.

NASA

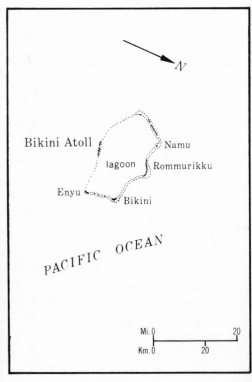

Oblique
Width of view: approx. 120 miles (193.1 kilometers)

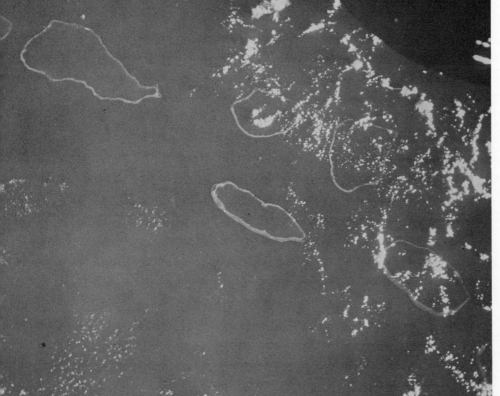

Bikini Atoll was the site of American nuclear testing between 1946 and 1958. Late in 1968, the people of Bikini, evacuated when testing began, were moved back to their devastated home.

NASA

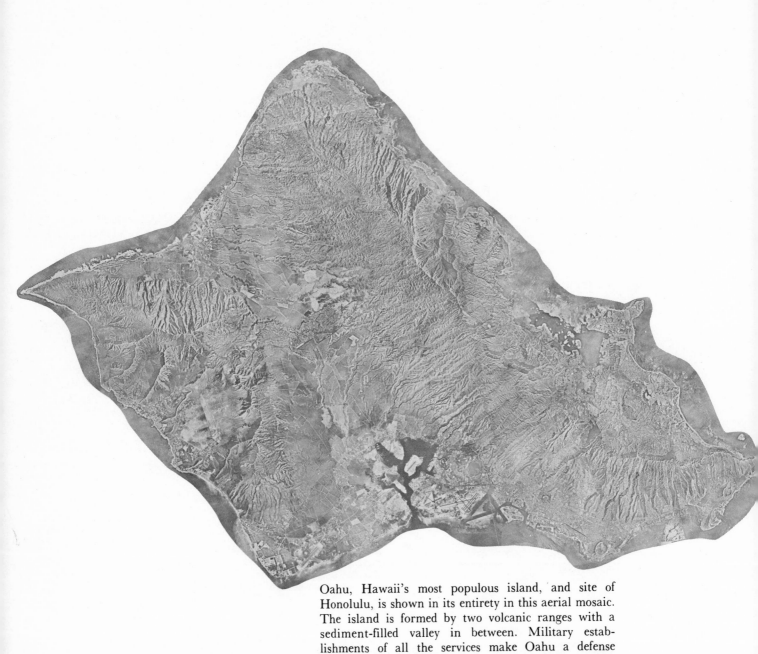

Oahu, Hawaii's most populous island, and site of Honolulu, is shown in its entirety in this aerial mosaic. The island is formed by two volcanic ranges with a sediment-filled valley in between. Military establishments of all the services make Oahu a defense bastion, and provide the state's chief source of revenue.

SCS, USDA

Hawaii

The American state of Hawaii has jurisdiction over most of the one hundred small and eight large islands of the Hawaiian group. Hawaii, the easternmost and largest island, is about twice the size of Delaware. Kure Island, at the other end of the chain, lies nearly 2,000 miles (3,218.6 kilometers) to the west of Hawaii, and is a 211-acre (85.3 hectare) atoll.

These islands are a demonstration of the reef and land-building process described by Charles Darwin after his voyage in the *Beagle*. From Kure east, the islands are atolls atop volcanic mountains with low elevations. These characteristics change to purely volcanic rocks, barely awash, in the center of the chain. The main islands are volcanic and younger in formation to the east until Hawaii, which has the still active, towering Mauna Kea cone. The islands grow eastward in height, with Mauna Loa, an extinct volcano on Hawaii, being the highest mountain in the chain at 13,796 feet (4,204.9 meters) above sea level. Further, although the ocean is deep near Kure, it deepens toward Hawaii to reach 18,876 feet (5,753 meters).

Noting this trend of youth toward the southeast, submarine geologists' investigations of the ocean floor east of Hawaii resulted in the discovery of seamounts, or undersea peaks, as an extension of the chain. Since Darwin's study of atolls suggested an evolutionary process, perhaps these seamounts will one day rise as volcanoes to form new islands.

Subtropical Hawaii has a mild climate and an attraction for tourists, and tourism has recently moved ahead of sugar and pineapple as the state's chief industry. Honolulu, the largest city in Oceania, has a population of about 300,000; Hilo, the second-largest city, has a population of 26,000. This disparity is partly owing to the larger natural anchorage of Pearl Harbor and to a more extensive area of level land available for settlement.

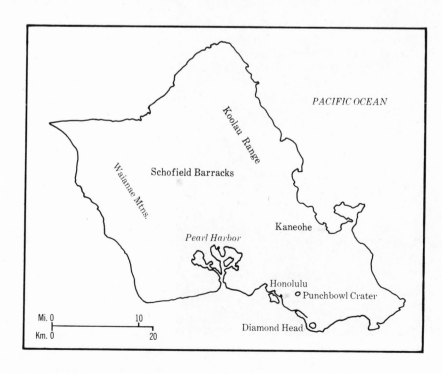

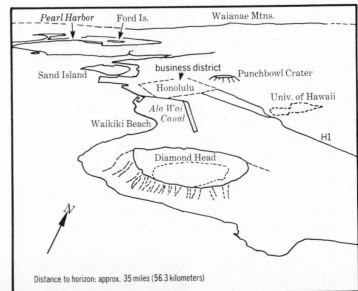

Diamond Head, a highly eroded extinct volcano, was designated a National Natural Landmark in 1968 to preserve it from an extension of the hotel complex of Waikiki. Offshore barrier reefs of coral show the region to be in a youthful stage of atoll development.

Robert A. Morris

Pearl Harbor   Ford Is.   Waianae Mtns.

Sand Island   business district   Punchbowl Crater

Honolulu   Univ. of Hawaii

Ala Wai Canal

Waikiki Beach   H1

Diamond Head

N

Distance to horizon: approx. 35 miles (56.3 kilometers)

Kure, the Midway Islands, and Pearl and Hermes Reef are the westernmost of the Hawaiian chain. They lie near the 180-degree meridian in the mid-Pacific, nearly 2,000 miles (3,218.7 kilometers) from Hawaii Island. Midway atoll consists of two low sand islands, and is under U.S. Navy administration. This group is the oldest part of the Hawaiian Islands.

NASA

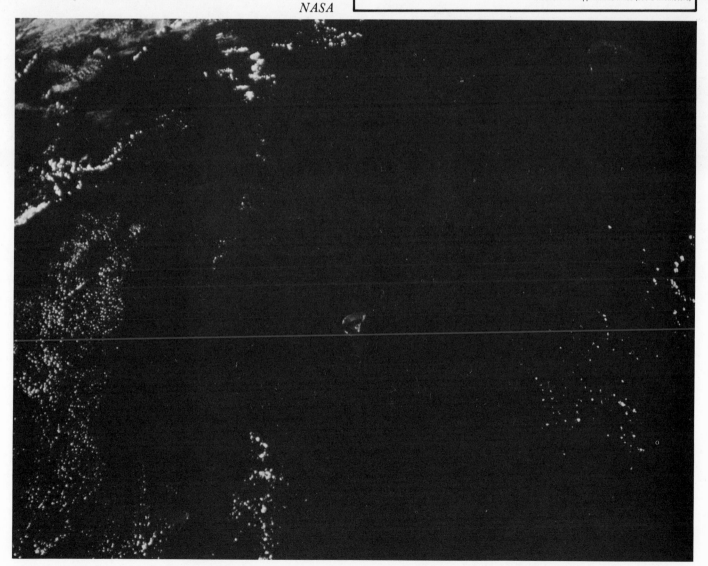

Pearl and Hermes Reef

PACIFIC OCEAN

Midway Islands

N

Kure Island   Oblique

Width of view: approx. 120 miles (193.1 kilometers)

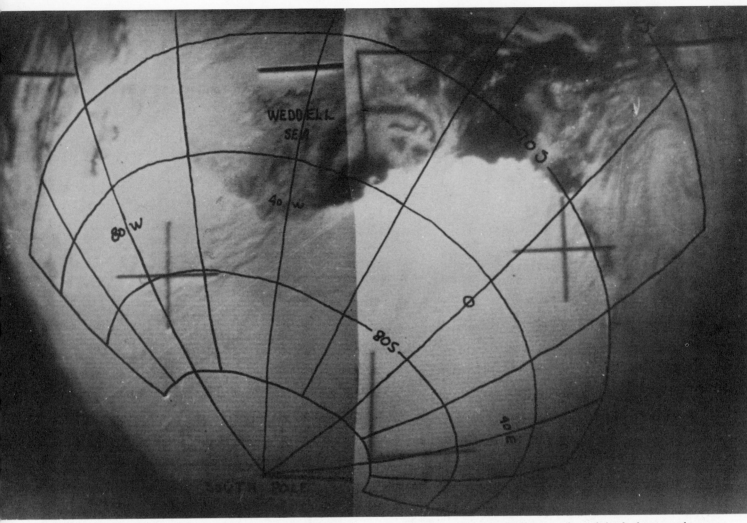

Most of Antarctica — the seventh continent — is shown in this Tiros 9 montage. The crosses and right angle marks are part of the camera's orientation system. Technicians at Goddard Space Flight Center added latitude and longitude lines to the original photograph. A cyclonic weather system is visible to the right, off Queen Maud Land in the South Atlantic.

NASA

Part VIII
THE POLAR REGIONS

There is no similarity between the Arctic and the Antarctic except a cold climate and the facts that both are the poles of the earth's magnetic field and the geographic poles. The Arctic is an ocean basin crossed by undersea ridges; the Antarctic is a mountainous continent a little less than twice the size of Australia.

The exploration of both polar regions and discovery of the Poles were dramatic events early in this century. In 1909, Robert Peary, Matthew Henson, and four Eskimos reached the North Pole. The South Pole was reached in 1911 by Roald Amundsen with a party of four men. By 1930 the first flights over both Poles had been made by Richard E. Byrd. These triumphs were preceded by a number of probing expeditions that surveyed the routes followed to the Poles.

Scientific examination and permanent habitation of the Arctic Ocean and Antarctica began in the 1950's. The purpose of polar studies is broad: animals, geology, ice characteristics, weather, men under isolated conditions, and the sea. Tremendous quantities of water are locked in the polar ice. Should the average temperature of the earth rise and the ice melt, the higher sea level would drown every coastal region in the world.

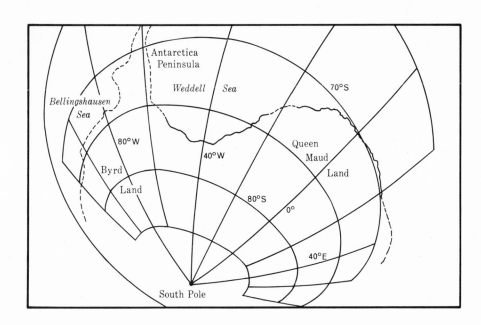

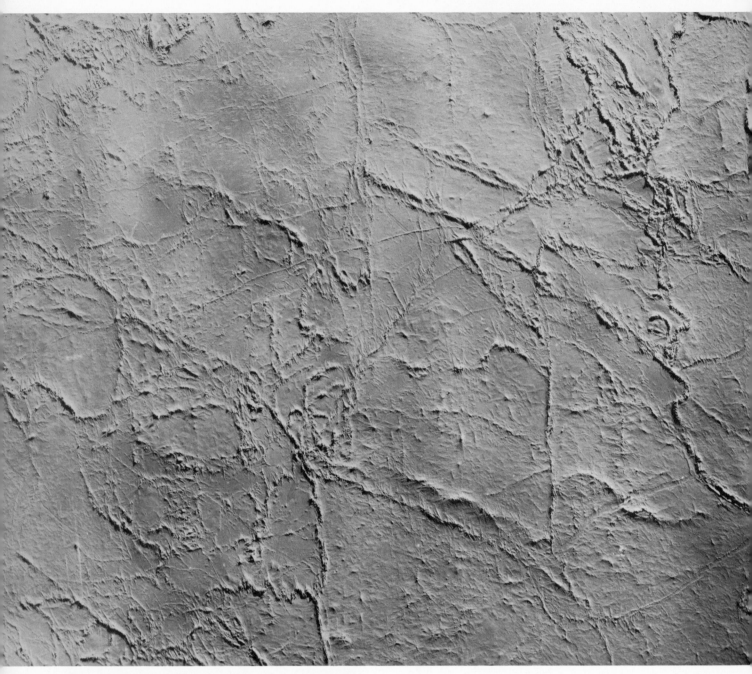

The rugged surface of the Arctic Sea ice is apparent in
this aerial view of the North Pole region. Snow-filled
cracks and pressure ridges of broken ice outline the edges
of broken floes. In constant motion owing to sea swells
and currents, the ice breaks apart and grinds together
again. Open water is occasionally noted at the Pole by
weather aircraft on routine flights.

U.S. Air Force Photograph

The Arctic

As a home for man, the Arctic is seemingly inhospitable and barren. In geographic terms it is a desert. Yet the Russian, Scandinavian and North American edges of the Arctic Sea are all inhabited by indigenous peoples. They have adapted to the extremities of the climate, and did not move south as did others who crossed the Bering Strait tens of thousands of years ago.

Several large islands of fresh-water ice in the Arctic Sea have been used for scientific stations by Americans and Russians since the late 1940's. The present American base is called T-3 or Fletcher's Ice Island. Lieutenant Colonel J.O. Fletcher lead the first party to land on the island. The T-3 designation is a reference to the discovery of the island by United States Navy radar in 1947 as Target 3.

The camp on T-3 was first established in 1952, removed in 1961, reestablished in 1962, and has been inhabited since. The path of the island, floating amid the thinner pack ice, and drifting with the current, carries it on a broad clockwise spiral path between Alaska and the Canadian Arctic and almost to the Pole.

T-3 is used as an oceanographic "ship," recording meteorological data and undersea conditions around the clock. Cameras are lowered through holes in the 100 feet (30.5 meters) thick ice to photograph the sea floor. Temperature and salinity studies are also made from T-3.

Depth recorder traces, taken from T-3 in its travels, have given geologists a picture of the northwestern Arctic sea floor. Coupled with analysis of the structure of the Canadian Arctic islands, the geology of the Arctic shows a history similar to that of other oceans. Soviet scientists on ships and other ice islands have made similar discoveries. The Arctic is composed of two large basins bisected by the transpolar underwater Lomonosov Ridge, which is flanked by depressed parallel basins on either side. On the outer sides of the basins are two mountain ranges. The Nansen Cordillera to the east is an extension of the mid-ocean ridge in the Atlantic. The Alpha Cordillera, discovered from T-3, extends from Ellesmere Island, Canada, to the continental shelf of northern Siberia. It too is a mid-ocean ridge.

Activity in the Arctic is not limited to the surface and sea floor. The American submarine *Nautilus* reached the Pole under the ice in 1958. In 1959 the submarine *Skate* surfaced at the Pole, followed by the *Seadragon* in 1961 and the *Wolf* in 1969. Regular flights near or over the Pole are made by United States Air Force weather planes and commercial airliners.

During the winter and spring of 1968-1969, a British expedition lead by Wally Herbert made the first over-ice crossing of the Arctic via the Pole. In 1968 an American-Canadian expedition lead by Ralph Plaisted reached the Pole by snowmobiles before being airlifted to Canada.

The ice surface of the Arctic is seldom smooth. Great floes are broken up by storms and thrown into linear mounds called "pressure ridges." Long, narrow open water leads and wide, oval

Airborne polar expeditions, to test equipment and make meteorological and ice observations, land at the North Pole from time to time. The monotony of the ice surface is apparent in this low-level aerial view. In the center of the picture, stacked oil drums make a temporary monument on the drifting ice at the Pole.

U.S. Air Force photograph

223

polynyas diverge to relieve sidewise pressure on the pack, but also provide weak spots to be filled. At the southern limit, floes break off and join icebergs from Greenland and Canadian glaciers to menace shipping lanes in the North Atlantic.

Although the Arctic Ocean has its greatest value in scientific and military fields, the southern edge of the sea provides a shipping lane that circles the ocean. The North American segment, called the Northwest Passage, was sought for centuries before being discovered in the 1850's. It was not actually traversed until Roald Amundsen succeeded in 1903-1906. In 1969 and 1970 the jumbo tanker *Manhattan* became the first commercial vessel to traverse the route and to return.

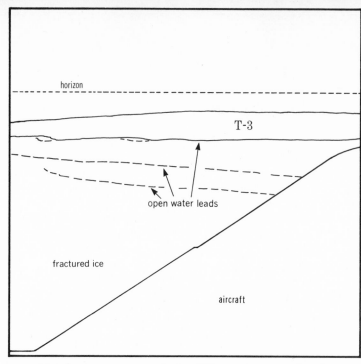

Ice island T-3 shows a relatively smooth surface amid the dark leads of open water and fractured surface of Arctic ice. T-3 was first discovered in 1947 near Ellesmere Land, Canada, and has been used as a floating research station almost continuously since 1952. Ice islands are stronger and of a different structure than ice floes. Several other ice islands have been visited by American or Soviet scientists, but for shorter lengths of time.

Lamont-Doherty Geologic Observatory

Antarctica

Seismic soundings of the ice show that Antarctica is like other land masses except for the ice burden that has depressed the crust of the earth under the continent. The thickest ice lies over the subglacial trough on the Pacific side of the Pole where it is 14,000 feet (4,267.2 meters) through. On the main landmass the thickness is irregular but often well over 3,000 feet (914.4 meters), with the average ice thickness estimates at 6,500 feet (1,981.2 meters).

Several seismic traverses across the icecap have given geologists profiles from which tentative constructions of the shape of the land beneath can be judged. Apparently the Indian and Atlantic Ocean section of Antarctica is an ancient basic rock mass, but the Antarctic Peninsula is younger. Between the two lies the Byrd Subglacial Basin.

The shape of the Antarctic Peninsula is a mirror image of the tip of South America and is considered by some geologists to be part of the Andean system of mountains. Recent evidence bolstering this view has been volcanic activity on the Peninsula and across the subglacial basin on the edge of the Ross Sea. These eruptions plus extinct volcanoes fill a gap in the volcanic chain encircling the Pacific.

About 200 to 160 million years ago the Antarctic climate was tropical enough for ferns to grow. Some of these and other large plants

South Pole Station, a U.S. Navy establishment, has been occupied since 1956, when the first Americans to reach the Pole landed from navy aircraft. For a few years the Pole itself was distinguished by a black and orange "barber pole" erected by the late Dr. Paul Siple, the first civilian station leader and a Princeton alumnus. Shifting ice has moved the polar station toward South America at the rate of about 150 feet (45.7 meters) per year.

Official U.S. Navy Photograph

became the continent's coal deposits. In 1967 the fossil jawbone of a fresh-water amphibian was discovered and in 1969 the finding of a fossil insect wing was announced. Similar fossils in Australia and South Africa, and similarities between rocks of the other continents, are excellent proof of continental drift. Antarctica was once part of Gondwanaland, and was evidently joined to Southern Africa. Over millions of years it drifted in a great loop around the Pole to its present site and turned about ninety degrees eastward in the process.

During the Southern Hemisphere winter, impassable pack ice surrounds the coast of Antarctica. In this aerial photograph, the decorative pattern of new ice is being cut by the U.S. Navy icebreaker *Edisto,* making a path for the icebreaker USCG *Northwind* and the British research-and-supply vessel *John Biscoe.* This cooperative effort is typical of the internationalized, boundaryless continent.

Official U.S. Navy Photograph

McMurdo Station, the chief American supply base in Antarctica, lies below a volcanic cone on the edge of the Ross Sea. In the distance, across the Ross Ice Shelf, are the peaks of Victoria Land. McMurdo is a small town with social and intellectual conveniences found in many American communities. Electric power is generated by an atomic power plant whose wastes are shipped to the United States for disposal.

Official U.S. Navy Photograph

APPENDIX I

A Brief Summary of the Earth Sciences

The term "earth sciences" represents the inter-disciplinary approach to our planet of today's physical scientists. Geology, geography, geomorphology, oceanography, meteorology, and their specialist subdivisions are overlapping disciplines devoted to the study of our planet.

The earth is a sphere about 8,000 miles (12,874.7 kilometers) in diameter, surrounded by a gaseous atmosphere we call "air." The part of the earth we know best is the relatively thin, hardened crust that covers the molten rock of the mantle which in turn surrounds a somewhat more solid inner and outer core. The principal physical features of the earth's surface are the oceans and continents. Under the continents the crust is thicker but lighter than under the oceans. It is thickest of all under the great mountain ranges of the world.

The prevalent scientific view (only a few years old) of the earth's crust is that it is a mosaic of six large and a few smaller segments, or plates. The plates are dominated by the continental land masses and extend to mid-ocean with the prominent exception of the Pacific Ocean basin. Along the Asian and South America coast, the continental and oceanic plates meet with the seaward crust dipping into a very deep trench and under the continent.

The plate concept developed from the continental drift theory, whose acceptance during the late 1960's marked a major scientific advance. First seriously proposed about forty-five years ago, the drift theory used geologic evidence to support the view that the present continents were once-joined parts of larger land masses. Over the past 300 million years the continents drifted to their present positions as the oceans opened up. Today we know a world-circling mid-ocean ridge system with a central rift valley is the source of new crustal material as the sea floor spreads and "floats" the continents farther apart. In this atlas

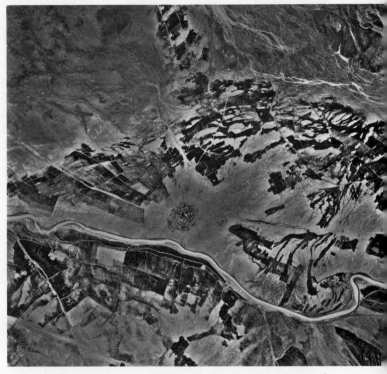

A single aerial photograph may have value in a variety of scientific fields. This view of Mandali, Iraq, shows the village, with its mosque in the center, and fields that indicate agricultural and landholding patterns. It illustrates the arid climate by lack of ground cover. Since no bridges or paved roads are visible, travel is by animal. The river is probably shallow, which enables workers to reach fields on the far bank from the village. These are some of the more obvious aspects of geography apparent in the photograph. A geologist might note the direction of stream flow, the straightness of the course, the field patterns, and texture of the landforms to deduce some aspects of local geology. From a photograph such as this, a very accurate map of the area could be prepared.

Fairey Surveys, Ltd.

227

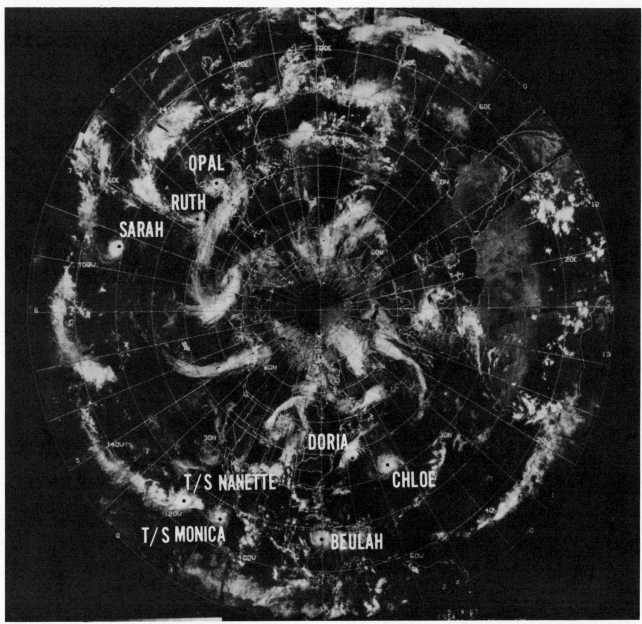

OPAL
RUTH
SARAH
DORIA
T/S NANETTE
CHLOE
T/S MONICA
BEULAH

several above-water examples of drift are shown in aerial photographs.

Before the creation of the present continents, two great land masses, Laurasia, in the Northern Hemisphere, and Gondwanaland, in the Southern Hemisphere, rose above the oceans. But these protocontinents developed as part of a continuing process which began when the earth's crust first began to form about 3,500 million years ago.

Throughout the history of the earth, the geologic processes that shape the land surface were actively raising mountains only to erode them to level plains, which were then raised and warped to form newer ranges. Most of the world's mountains are formed from layers of sand, silt,

One day's weather over most of the Northern Hemisphere is visible in a single satellite photograph. Actually, this picture is a mosaic compiled by computer from data supplied by the ESSA 5 weather satellite on September 14, 1967. In addition to printing out the tones of the mosaic, the computer "draws" in geographical outlines, latitude and longitude lines, and prints coordinate numbers. Eight major storms are visible in this photograph. The rotation of each storm and its path across the globe can be plotted from a succession of photographs such as this one.

ESSA

and the remains of marine creatures carried by ancient seas into great troughs, called geosynclines. Often currents in the mantle squeezed on the sides of the trough, forcing the layered

228

beds of sedimentary rock to rise and wrinkle into great ridges. The Himalayas, Canadian Rockies, and other prominent ranges show sections of old sedimentary beds high on their peaks. Other ranges, such as the Sierra Nevada of California, are remnants of once-molten material forced up into sedimentary beds that have long since eroded away.

Geologists have created a time scale for the earth's rocks based on fossil remains of plants and animals found in sedimentary beds. This scale deals only in thousands and millions of years. The earliest fossils, found in older rocks, can be traced by their evolution (or extinction) through the sequence of younger rocks. In this way rocks can be dated, whether they are on mountain tops or part of a well core. Where fossils are rare or absent, radiometric dating, using the half-life decay of minerals in the rock, shows the age of the sample. Nonfossiliferous rock such as lava can be dated by the age of the beds into which it intrudes or which it overlies.

Although geologists refer to epochs of the past by name, for simplicity the dates of these periods in years have been used in this atlas instead of the names. A table listing the epochs and time scale will be found in standard reference works and large dictionaries.

Erosion is a weather-caused process that, in ideal terms, levels the mountains. Obviously no man has seen this happen, and geologists use examples of mountains at different stages of erosion to describe various steps in the process. Climate and latitude are important elements of erosion since the same type of rock is worn away differently in a hot and arid climate than where it is moist and either cold, mild, or hot.

In some parts of the world an important erosional factor has been the most recent sequence of continental glaciation when great ice sheets alternately covered the land and melted, to finally retreat to the present dimensions of the polar regions. A lesser but dramatic erosional factor has been faulting of crustal movement along fractures in the crust. Movement along the fault plane causes a shock wave we call an earthquake. Alterations in drainage patterns, uplift of mountains, and depression of valleys are the chief visible results of faulting.

Geomorphology is the science dealing with surface landforms. Throughout this atlas, basic landform types are described and shown in aerial photographs.

Probably the most familiar of the earth sciences is geography — the study of man's relationship to the earth. This science encompasses some aspects of all the other earth sciences. For the professional geographer, data is presented in symbols, statistical maps, and diagrams. Geographic descriptions in this atlas present the material as captions and text, with the photographs as a visual demonstration. Each of the pictures shows far more information than is possible to describe in the text.

Meteorology is one earth science able to utilize to very good advantage aerial photography — especially from satellites. Implementation of the international World Weather Watch and the development of inexpensive satellite picture receivers are providing a valuable addition to established meteorological and climatological techniques. Naturally, most of the useful data from satellites are pictures of clouds and storm systems. Clear-weather studies are based on radiosonde (balloon-borne automatic signal transmitters) and observations from aircraft and ground stations. But satellite photography is able to function even on the nightside of the earth, and the promise of future improvement in weather satellite functions is great.

As the chief erosional force, weather operates in a complex interplay with the oceans and the shape of the land surface, and varies seasonally and differentially over the globe. The end result of weather is climate — the average of the weather for a given region.

Most weather occurs at altitudes low enough to be partially blocked by mountains, with a clear path across plains and the sea. Part of this topographic influence is reflected in the hydrological cycle when water evaporated from the sea falls as rain or snow in greater amounts on one slope of a mountain range than on the other. In this atlas the various aspects of weather as an agent of erosion and as climate are described as well as shown in photographs. Furthermore, individual weather patterns are shown in some of the photographs.

APPENDIX II

The Uses of Aerial Photography

To millions of people today the aerial view of cities, mountains, coastlines, and rivers is as familiar as the ground-level appearance. And often the vista is one never seen from the ground, especially for those flying over remote or inhospitable terrain. Part of the purpose of this book is to provide the airborne, as well as the armchair traveler, with general clues to the aerial view of our planet.

The photographs in this atlas have been selected to show different aspects of world geography, townscapes, and weather. Photographs in this Appendix illustrate some of the uses of aerial photography.

In the past hundred years, aerial photography advanced from balloon-borne wet-plate cameras to high-speed aircraft with complex camera systems to color photography from orbiting spacecraft. The uses of aerial photographs multiplied quickly as their value to scientists and engineers was recognized. Pioneering efforts in various fields began just after the turn of the century, but

These three photographs of agricultural areas can be compared with others in this atlas to show political as well as technical differences in land distribution. At the top are the long narrow fields of Province de Québec, Canada. These are more like the fields of France than the irregular plots of the former British possession of Malta (center). The Maltese farm their hillsides by creating terrace-like fields. The lack of forests shows the necessity for maximum use of tillable ground. Below is an aerial view of a banana plantation in Cameroon, Africa. The herbaceous plants have been set out in rows. Random trees stand above the low-growing banana, which yields only a single crop per plant. White rectangles are fieldworkers' homes.

Top. NAPL A16848-24; center and bottom,
Fairey Surveys, Ltd.

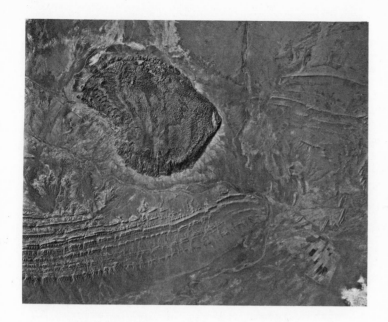

The advantages of aerial photography for geologic studies are seen in this view of a salt plug near Qum, Iran. Salt plugs are intrusive features forced up through sedimentary beds. Valuable quantities of petroleum products are often found in association with buried plugs. In the photograph the dimensions of the plug, local geologic structure, and roads giving access are visible.

Fairey Surveys, Ltd.

most of the development has been in the past twenty-five years.

The greatest use of aerial photographs is for photogrammetry, or aerial surveying. An accurate aerial photograph, used as a map base, is worth months of effort by a ground survey crew, especially if the terrain is rugged, wet, cold, or remote.

Maps made from aerial photographs are drawn by complex electromechanical instruments that calculate differences in elevation automatically from stereoscopic photo prints. Under the control of the operator, these plotters draw contour lines connecting points of equal elevation. With names, symbols, and shading added to the contour map (by using other electronic devices), a finished piece of artwork is ready for the map printer in a fraction of the time necessary to complete a map drawn by hand.

Another time advantage of aerial surveys over field work is in scientific and engineering surveys whose results show locations of interest for possible on-site inspection. In geology, aerial photographs show potential mineral deposits, possible dam sites, and classic geologic forms for student study. The first photographs of a site also form a record against which later ground operations can be checked.

Geographers make use of aerial photographs in their study of human activity; of catastrophic changes after earthquakes, floods, storms; and in surveys of land use. Foresters use aerial photographs for timber cruising, with special scales made to count trees, tree sizes, and even to estimate the yield of a proposed logging operation. Also, diseased trees and plants are revealed in aerial photographs, thereby suggesting remedial measures. A similar use is in agriculture, where the effects of fertilizer and pesticides can be determined. In Africa disastrous crop destruction by locusts may ultimately be halted when newly begun aerial surveys learn more about the insects' life cycle and habits.

One of the most fascinating aspects of aerial photography is its use in archaeology. Ancient sites, long concealed under plowed fields, desert sands, or vegetation, are often visible from the air but not from the ground. Subtle differences in basic colors of crops, faint shadows under a low sun, and soil disturbances reveal walls, building foundations, fences, and travel routes.

In heavily populated regions with adequate

231

A unique advantage of aerial photography in archaeology is that many sites are visible only from the air, as in this view of part of Berkshire, England. The diagram points out and identifies ancient field outlines, probably of medieval, or earlier, origin. This photograph also shows the distinctive pattern difference in tree types when viewed from the air.

Fairey Surveys, Ltd.

In aerial photographs used for oceanographic and estuarine research, the pictures are often of transitory events. Thus a succession of photographs must be taken at periodic intervals for several seasons to gain an accurate view of the area. This is a negative-print view of Saint-Pierre harbor, Île de Saint-Pierre. The island, with those of Miquelon and Langlade, is a French possession off Newfoundland, Canada, in the Gulf of Saint Lawrence. By reversing the black-and-white tones of the photograph, the pattern of wave and wind patterns is made more striking than if the tones were "normal."

A13447-69 NAPL

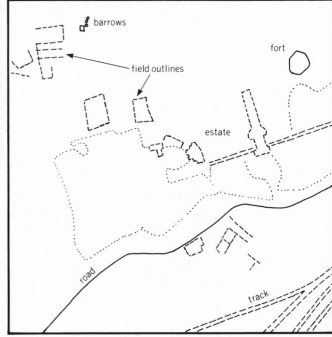

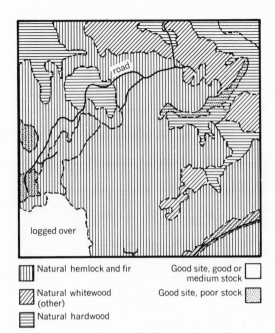

road

logged over

	Natural hemlock and fir		Good site, good or medium stock
	Natural whitewood (other)		Good site, poor stock
	Natural hardwood		

Aerial photography is a particularly useful tool for examining the world's natural resources. As used in forest management, photographs such as this one of a "tree farm" in Washington are used to determine tree-types, and to estimate timber available for lumber and choice of sites for replanting. The diagram shows analysis of the site made by a professional forester.

Weyerhaeuser Company, Timberland Division

maps, aerial photographs are used for re-surveying, town planning, and pollution control. To the engineer who must do the work, and the politician who must find the funds and write the laws, aerial photography is an especially valuable tool. The increased use of color aerial photography is dramatizing the need for pollution control.

For regions with little population but great economic potential, aerial surveys are the first step in avoiding chaotic growth or exploitation. A guiding force in this work has been the Cartography Section of the Resources and Transport Division, a part of the United Nations' Department of Economic and Social Affairs. The Section provides technical assistance to a number of countries under a program that uses the most modern techniques of cartography and of interpretation of photographs. One object is to train the participating countries' nationals.

A continuing series of regional technical conferences is held under United Nations sponsorship annually, with technical papers and seminars stimulating exchange of information.

In summary it is safe to say that aerial photographs are becoming the mid-twentieth century's way of looking at the world.

Index

Cross references in this Index are intended to permit the reader to find photographs which show similar or related geologic trends, weather patterns, urban areas, types of agriculture, and the like.